THE NEW CATHEDRAL BASIC READERS

CURRICULUM FOUNDATION SERIES
REG. U. S. PAT. OFF.

More People and Progress

CATHEDRAL EDITION

The Reverend John A. O'Brien

A revision of More People and Progress

William S. Gray, Marion Monroe, A. Sterl Artley
May Hill Arbuthnot

SCOTT, FORESMAN AND COMPANY

Chicago Atlanta Dallas Palo Alto Fair Lawn, N.J.

Contents

World Neighbors

The World of Nature

Men of Progress

In the Shadow of the Cathedrals

Old Tales from Many Lands

World Neighbors

Kaatje's Adventure

"Kaatje! Hurry up!" Karel's voice
called impatiently to his sister.

Kaatje picked up her unaccustomed full petticoats
and clattered down the brick path. "Coming!"
she called, running as fast as she could in the big
wooden shoes that seemed so clumsy.

Kaatje was as eager as her brother to get started.
This was an important day. Their Koopdam village
school had six grades, and today a teacher was
taking the three upper ones to the flower fair in
the town of Bloemen. There they would take part in
a program of songs and dances in the town square.

For this big affair old costumes of Holland had
come out of trunks and attics. The petticoats and
tight bodice were well suited to Kaatje's sturdy

6

figure. The crisply starched white cap made a pretty frame for her blond braids and blue eyes.

The long ballooning trousers and silver-buttoned jacket also suited Karel, with his square chin, gray eyes, and bushy yellow hair that he tried so hard to control. In his costume he resembled a youth of long ago.

The children's part in the fair had been the idea of their teacher, *Juffrouw* Van Hoorn. For weeks she had been drilling them in old-time songs and dances; and she had written to her uncle, a member of the town council of Bloemen, telling him about her plan. Then *Mynheer* Van Hoorn had sent a special invitation and a letter. His letter said that he was hiring a barge to carry the children through the canals from Koopdam to Bloemen.

It was all very exciting, and Kaatje could hardly wait to be on her way. But when she said good-by to her younger brother and sister, they looked so forlorn that she had to run back to comfort them. "Don't you mind," she whispered. "Kaatje will bring you presents."

She was feeling very rich, for Uncle Hans had given her two whole guilders to spend on her trip. She had intended to use her money for chocolate candy filled with nuts. However, after seeing the sorrowful faces of the two children, she had decided to buy them something instead.

"Hurry!" said Karel. "Do you want to make us both late? We'll have to run now!"

Kaatje felt like making a sharp reply. But running with wooden shoes and full petticoats was hard enough without trying to talk. However, her thoughts were busy. Karel seemed to think he was boss, and Kaatje did not like it. After all, he was only a year older—scarcely twelve; so he should not act as if he were her grandfather.

The barge that waited at the edge of the small Koopdam canal looked gay with its orange-and-blue paint and its flags flying. Already the children were surging on board. They were all in high spirits, shouting greetings and laughing over the unusual costumes.

The young people started to sing as the barge began to move. It went slowly through the small canal and then out into a larger one.

Passing through tiny villages with neat houses of rose-red brick and gaily painted garden gates was exciting to Kaatje. In the fields she counted dozens of windmills. But Karel told her that a good many of them were standing idle now, since most farmers used electricity. She saw flowers everywhere. The meadows, the gardens, the windows, and the carts of village flower sellers were overflowing with colorful blooms.

"I've never seen so many tulips before!" Kaatje exclaimed.

"It's like this all the way to Bloemen," said Karel. "I've taken this canal trip several times," he added with pride.

Kaatje's reply was a sigh of envy. Boys certainly had all the best of it, she thought resentfully. A girl never had any real adventures.

Suddenly *Juffrouw* Van Hoorn interrupted these thoughts by calling out, "Line up at once! Each class together! Karel, you are the leader of yours. Come up here, please!"

Wooden shoes clumped, petticoats swished as the youngsters rushed up to take their places. In all the excitement of landing, Karel and his sister soon lost sight of each other.

What a day it was! First came the big flower parade through the streets of Bloemen. The school children, all bedecked with bright garlands, marched

briskly along the route of
the parade. Behind them
came a long, long line
of flower-covered cars,
carts, wagons,
and trucks.

As Kaatje
marched, she kept
looking for a toyshop
where she might buy gifts
to take to the little children
at home. Soon she saw a display of toys in a window. There
was a boat that would delight young
Frans. Surely she could find something nice
for Annetje, too.

10

After the parade, folk dancing and singing took place in the public square. A picnic lunch was provided by the town councilmen; then came more songs and dances. Later there were rides on the wonderful Ferris wheel. Kaatje managed to be one of the first to ride. Then while the other children swarmed about, waiting for their turns, she slipped away without a word to anyone.

Somehow the toyshop seemed farther away than she remembered. Her feet were tired from dancing and walking in the wooden shoes. But she reached the place at last and soon had the little ship bought for Frans. Annetje's present took more time. Finally Kaatje chose a toy baking set. She clutched her packages and hurried away, realizing uneasily that her shopping had taken longer than she had planned.

Surely she must be nearing the big public square. She listened anxiously for sounds of singing or at least of talking and laughing. But everything was quiet. When she reached the square, she saw to her dismay that the school children were gone.

Back she clumped toward the canal, wishing with all her heart that she had gone straight to the canal from the shop. Yet who would have thought that all the children could disappear so suddenly? How could she possibly have missed them on their way to the barge?

Then Kaatje recalled that *Mynheer* Van Hoorn had promised to take all the Koopdam boys and girls back to the barge in cars when the fun was over. They probably had passed the toyshop while she was searching for Annetje's gift.

She walked as fast as she could in the clumsy shoes. It could not be much farther now to the canal. "Everything will be fine once I get there," she told herself.

Nevertheless she still felt uneasy. If only she had told Karel beforehand where she was going! He often got out of patience with her, but she could depend on his help when she needed it.

At last she sighted the canal, crowded with big barges. Anxiously her eyes searched for the one from Koopdam.

Up and down she clumped! That barge had to be there some place. Any minute now she would find it, or someone on it would call to her. Surely it would not have gone without her. If only she could catch a glimpse of Karel!

In her anxiety Kaatje started to run. The next thing she knew, she had slipped on a wet spot; and with a splash, she found herself floundering about in the canal, frightened and gasping.

"Help! Help!" she shouted. "Help!"

"Don't be afraid! Can't you swim?" called a voice from the deck of a nearby barge.

12

Kaatje looked up to see
a dark-eyed lad about her own
age gazing down at her. A dog's
black face was close beside the boy's.

"Yes, of course I can swim," sputtered Kaatje
indignantly. "But—but——"

"All right then," said the boy. "Don't get mad.
I'll put down the ladder."

In a moment a short ladder was put over the
side. Kaatje struggled to reach it, but she made
little progress.

"Wait, I'll help you," said the boy.

He swung down the ladder; and reaching out a
hand, he helped Kaatje to the lowest rung and then
up onto the deck.

"Thank you—very much," gasped Kaatje, trying to get her breath.

The boy nodded, his face breaking into a smile as he looked at her. "It's no wonder you couldn't swim in that kind of bathing suit," he chuckled. "Tell me, what are you doing dressed up like that?"

"Our school came from Koopdam on a barge to take part in the flower fair today," explained Kaatje. "After the program I went shopping by myself, and it took longer than I thought. There are my packages floating in the water. I wish I had hung onto them."

"I'll get them," the boy offered, stripping off his shirt and shoes. Without another word, he dived into the canal and soon climbed aboard with the two soggy parcels.

Quickly Kaatje tore at the wet wrappings. "I want to find out if the presents I bought for my sister, Annetje, and my little brother, Frans, are all right," she said.

"Let me help," offered the boy. "Here, the toy ship is fine. Why shouldn't it be? A canal is just the place for ships."

"The baking set is tin. So it's all right," said Kaatje with relief. "Now the next thing is to find the barge I came on. That's what I was trying to do when I fell into the canal. The barge is orange and blue. Have you seen it?"

The boy gave a low whistle. "Yes, but I do believe it's gone away and left you!" he exclaimed.

To her dismay Kaatje felt tears starting. "Maybe it wasn't my barge," she faltered.

"I'm afraid it was," said the boy, his voice full of sympathy. "There were a lot of boys and girls on it dressed up the way you are." He looked at her anxiously. "But please don't cry," he begged.

For once Kaatje found it impossible to be cheerful. Here she was, stranded far away from home, while the barge steamed on without her. She was wet, cold, hungry, and thoroughly miserable.

The boy spoke up. "My father and mother are in town buying some supplies before we start off again. But my grandfather is here. He can tell us what to do about this. Come, we'll ask him." The boy started racing over the deck, the dog at his heels. "Oh, my name is Kees," he shouted back over his shoulder.

"Mine's Kaatje," the girl replied, running after Kees and his dog.

Kees' grandfather was asleep on a cot in the little cabin. He woke at the sound of running feet and stared at the two dripping-wet children.

"What is going on?" he asked good-humoredly.

Kaatje waited a little fearfully as Kees explained. Surely the grandfather would be vexed. But he said calmly, "First we'll get you both into dry clothes."

Getting into dry clothing was simple enough for Kees. But finding something for Kaatje was quite another matter. A blue woolen dress that belonged to Kees' mother was found, and Kaatje got into it. When she stumbled out on the deck, Kees and his grandfather could not help laughing.

Kees' mother was more than plump. So the blue dress drooped comically over the girl's shoulders and trailed on the floor.

"I hope your mother won't be upset about my wearing her dress," Kaatje said.

"I don't think so," chuckled Kees. "Here she comes now, with Father."

Kaatje looked up. A stocky, blond man and a neat, stout woman, both loaded with bundles, were walking rapidly toward the barge.

"Tck! Tck!" Kees' mother made clucking sounds and shook her head disapprovingly while she listened to Kaatje's story of the accident. "You should not have run away by yourself," she scolded, "and I'm sure you know it."

Kaatje nodded, her cheeks very red.

Kees quickly came to Kaatje's rescue. "But now that she has already done so, Mother, what are we to do about it?" he asked.

"Well, first I should say that we must let her family know. And next we must see about getting her home."

"I'm wearing your dress," Kaatje blurted out nervously.

"So I see," nodded the good woman. "I did not think it was yours." Then as her twinkling eyes met Kaatje's, she and the girl burst out laughing. Kees, with his father and grandfather, joined in, while the dog barked excitedly.

"I was thinking," Kees' father said, "that early tomorrow morning we are due to stop near Koopdam. We can put our little friend on a bus for home."

Kaatje gave a happy sigh. Overnight on a barge! What an adventure that would be! Even Karel had never done anything like that!

"Now come inside," said Kees' mother briskly. "We must make a fire and dry out those wet clothes of yours."

Kaatje gladly followed her into the cozy cabin of the barge.

"Listen!" the woman said suddenly. "I hear someone talking." She glanced out of the cabin window. "It is *Mynheer* Van Hoorn, who is on the town council."

She rushed out, and Kaatje heard her say, "Yes, the girl is here safe and sound! Yes, yes, tomorrow we will get her home."

When Kaatje went out on deck, Kees was busy putting the supplies away. He stopped and grinned at Kaatje.

"You had your friends in a fine fret!" the boy exclaimed. "Your teacher thought you were on board when the barge started. But when she counted noses and found yours missing, she notified her uncle. It was he who came down here looking for you. He will telephone your parents in Koopdam that you are safe and will be home tomorrow."

"I certainly seem to have made trouble for everyone," said Kaatje apologetically.

"Yes, you have made quite a lot," agreed Kees. "Yet I like such a girl better than one who never thinks of anything to do, or dares to do it."

At that praise Kaatje looked startled. Then she giggled. "I hope that my mother and *Juffrouw* Van Hoorn will feel the same way," she said. "And especially my brother Karel!"

A Heritage to Treasure

Rain streamed down the lattice panes and hid the heather-covered English hills as Michael and Angela flattened their noses against the window in their father's old nursery. They had arrived only last night to spend the summer with their grandparents. On their first day in the old manor house they had planned to explore the garden and perhaps find the entrance to the secret passage that Daddy had said led into the house. Now the rain made the first day seem long and the summer endless.

Grandfather stuck his head in at the door and said, "A rainy day is just right for exploring indoors. Why don't you come with me?"

They followed Grandfather down the wide stairway and into the dining room. "This room was the great hall in olden days," he told them. "The rest of the house has been built onto it."

The hall was very high with great oak beams and a pointed roof. At one end was a raised platform which Grandfather called a dais, and on which stood a huge oak table, black with age.

"That is where your ancestor, the first Lord of the Manor, and his family used to sit," Grandfather said. "The servants and retainers dined in the lower part of the hall.

"Sir Hugh lived in an age famous for its chivalry. King Edward III, who was ruling then, admired King Arthur so much that he decided he, too, would have an order of famous knights. So he founded 'The Order of the Garter.' It is still the highest honor our ruler can bestow."

On the wall hung Sir Hugh's own shield with the words *Servare Fidem*. Michael knew they meant "Keep Faith." But what caught his eye was the great two-handed sword that hung there, too.

"It's too heavy for you to lift," Grandfather said. "Here, try on Sir Hugh's mailed glove."

Grandfather lifted the metal glove from its peg and handed it to Michael.

"How could Sir Hugh hold a sword with this on!" cried Michael.

"It took practice," said Grandfather.

"But think of the protection it gave. If anyone struck his hand with a weapon, the heavy metal would turn aside the blow."

Later in the day the sun came out. Grandmother said she was going to cut flowers for the church and asked the children to take them to Father John at St. Michael's, which was just across the road. While

she was cutting the flowers she explained something
that had puzzled both Michael and Angela.

"St. Michael's is a private chapel for the manor
now," Grandmother said. "There was a time when
Catholics were persecuted in England. Chivalry
was forgotten and priests paid with their lives for
saying Mass. In those days St. Michael's was empty.
But the people had their Mass. There were still
priests in hiding. One came to the manor house
whenever he could, by way of the secret passage.
Then when all the world was asleep, the villagers
came here to assist at the Holy Sacrifice. Years
later your great-grandfather was allowed to buy the
church as a chapel for the manor." Her basket was
full of flowers now. She handed it to Angela.

Michael looked thoughtful. "'Keep Faith,'" he
said softly, repeating the family motto. "Those
words mean more to me now, Grandmother."

At the rectory Father John was delighted to see
the children, whom he had not seen since they were
small. "I baptized you both," he said. "How
you've grown since then! Would you like to see the
font at which you were baptized?"

As they walked through the rectory garden, Father
John pointed to the yew trees all round the church.

"The yeomen of England made their bows from
our yews in the olden days," he said. "There was
archery practice here every Sunday after Mass.

"I don't think you would have liked living in those days, Michael. King Edward III made a law forbidding the playing of football because people were neglecting their archery for it. English archers were the finest in Europe, and it would never have done for them to get out of practice!"

They walked round the church and looked at the great west door. "What an enormous knocker," said Michael, looking at a huge bronze ring.

"If you hold that ring in your hands and go down on your knees, you will be doing what many a poor outlaw did in days gone by," said the priest.

"Like this?" asked Michael, kneeling before the door and clasping the ring.

"Just so! Now you are taking sanctuary! That is a 'sanctuary knocker.' If any poor fugitive from justice, that is, anyone who had broken the law and was running away, reached a church in time to seize the sanctuary knocker, he was safe. No one would dare to touch him, since he had appealed to Holy Church. It did not mean that he would never be punished, but that he would be safe for a certain number of days. At the end of that time the anger of his pursuers would have had a chance to cool, and he would be more likely to have a just trial."

They went into the church, and when they had knelt for a moment before the Blessed Sacrament, Father John showed them the old font, beautifully carved on its eight sides. "You see," he added, "Baptism is the way into the Church. That is why the font should always stand near the entrance and as far as possible from the altar. This font is about seven hundred years old, and most of your ancestors were baptized here. Let's say a prayer for them before we go."

When the children got home, Grandfather said he would show them one of his greatest treasures. "Come and help me get it," he said, and he led the way into the library. The walls were panelled in oak, and there were books all around the room except on either side of the fireplace. There the panelling was carved in the shape of fruit and flowers.

"There is a secret hiding place in the panelling which only the eldest son of the family knows how to find," he said. "You may watch me open it, but you won't be able to discover how it is done. You are the eldest, Michael, and the only son of my only son. Your father will tell you the secret on your twenty-first birthday."

As Grandfather passed his hand over the carved woodwork, a panel moved aside slowly, revealing an iron door. Grandfather took a key from his watch chain and opened the door to a hidden cupboard. He took down a large parcel wrapped in soft leather, and brought it to his writing desk.

"This is so valuable that it ought to be in the British Museum," he said, "but your Grandmother and I cannot bear to part with it."

He unwrapped the package with the greatest care, and there was a book! The cover was of dark-brown leather, with patterns stamped all down the front. In the middle was a picture of King David playing his harp. There was no title, but Grandfather said none was needed. "No one could take it for anything but a book of psalms," he said. "Do you remember how David used to play to King Saul when he was ill and troubled? The Psalms of David have soothed many troubled hearts since then. One of Sir Hugh's sons was a monk, and he made this book, copying down the psalms and decorating the pages."

"He helped keep the faith, too, in a way," said Angela, thinking of the family motto.

The children watched fascinated as Grandfather opened the book. He allowed them to examine a page through a magnifying glass, and they saw the amazing detail of the border. There was a castle and a tiny lake with swans on it, and many other scenes, all painted by the monk's careful hand.

As Grandfather closed the book, Michael realized with a start that the day was over, and he had not even begun to search for the secret passage.

"Thank you, Grandfather," he said. "I didn't realize how many interesting things there are here. It's a good thing we'll be here all summer."

Two Days to Remember

"Ah, Tonto, tomorrow will be a day for me to remember," Pepe said excitedly while unloading fruit from his donkey. "Tomorrow I shall have money to spend for myself alone."

The little donkey stamped impatiently and pulled on the rope that Pepe had looped around a sapling and knotted tightly.

"Too bad, Tonto, that you are tied up," Pepe said sympathetically. "But we start to market at daybreak. I'll have no time to hunt for you then."

As Tonto jerked his head in protest, Pepe gave him a friendly pat. Then the lad strode toward the house and placed a bunch of bananas on some outside shelves made of rough boards.

Swiftly the Puerto Rican boy stacked all the fruit that he had gathered from the hillsides. As he arranged it in neat rows on shelves so that nothing could happen to it during the night, his thoughts were busy with the day to come.

Tomorrow he would sell his fruit at the market. He would use the money to buy new shoes made of leather. Now that he was a high-school student, his old canvas shoes were no longer suitable. He needed a notebook, too, and perhaps some pencils. He could not decide what he should do with the money he hoped to have left over. Confused, happy thoughts raced through his mind. He could buy a kite. Or he might buy a fountain pen like the one Anita López had—a red one with a gold point.

"Maybe there will even be a few pennies extra," thought Pepe wistfully. "Then if I see the peddler, I shall buy a cup of sweet, red, shaved ice."

Pepe finished his work and turned to the house, where a lighted lantern cast a golden circle before the door. Inside all was dark and quiet, for Pepe's mother, father, and younger brothers and sisters were now asleep.

"They are not going to market," thought Pepe, "or they, too, would be making preparations."

After Pepe had blown out the lantern, he slipped indoors. Lifting the mosquito net from around his cot, he crept inside. There he lay listening to the perpetual tick-tick-ticking of the noisy old alarm clock until he fell asleep.

The blackness of night still filled the house when the alarm blared. Pepe hurriedly turned it off. He lifted his clean shirt and trousers from the nail on the plaster wall and went outdoors.

After lighting the oil lantern at the door, the boy washed himself with water from a jar on the shelf and put on his clean clothes. By that time his mother had awakened and had built a charcoal fire in the stone stove beside the house. The rich, strong odor of boiling coffee filled the morning air.

Soon Pepe's mother handed him his breakfast of rice and sweetened beans, piled high on a fresh banana leaf.

Suddenly, with no sign of dawn, the bright light of morning appeared. It was time for Pepe to be on his way. After slinging two big baskets across the donkey's back, he filled them with the coconuts, oranges, and limes he had previously gathered. On top he lashed two bunches of bananas.

Then Pepe put on his big straw hat. He tied the strings of his canvas shoes together and hung them around his neck. He would need them later when he reached the hot concrete streets in town. Finally he picked several oranges from a tree near the house and tucked them inside his shirt. These he would eat along the way.

"*Adiós!*" shouted Pepe, waving to his mother as he led his donkey away from the house.

The narrow road dipped and curved sharply downward. Sometimes there was a sheer drop to dizzy depths on one side, while steep crags rose on the other. For a time the road ran through a jungle. Here tree ferns grew in profusion. Low coffee trees stood in the deep shade of the taller plants. At the edge of the road Pepe plucked some flame-red flowers and twined them into Tonto's halter.

"You must look fine on market day, Little One," Pepe said. Then they went on, picking their way carefully down the steep, winding road. The vivid flowers stood up gaily between Tonto's ears, which flip-flopped with every step he took.

By and by they came to a small promontory near the sea. Then Pepe heard a low, moaning sound that he had never heard before. The strange noise persisted, and Pepe noticed that a strong wind was blowing from the southeast. In that direction the sky was a sickly yellow along the horizon.

"Could that be a hurricane blowing up?" the lad wondered. "No, Tonto," he said, trying to convince himself that his fears were imaginary. "Not in your time nor in mine has a big blow come to this part of Puerto Rico. Surely such a catastrophe cannot happen today of all days."

Pepe continued to be alarmed, however. He had heard his father tell about the big hurricane that had come long, long ago. It had brought the sea far up onto the land, washing away houses, crops, and highways. It had demolished buildings and had beaten the sugar cane in the fields to a pulp.

Soon Pepe forgot about the moaning noise, the darkening sky, and the strong wind. Through an opening in the trees he glimpsed the bright-colored houses of the town. Around the next bend in the road would be the big white house of *Señor* López. This was the plantation where Pepe's father came each day to cut sugar cane. Pepe was in classes at school with Anita López, who had once let him try out her red fountain pen with the gold point.

Pepe was glad that he was near the plantation. He could have a refreshing drink from the brook that plummeted down in a waterfall by the road and flowed on through a pipe to the López house. But suddenly the wind beat so hard against him that he could scarcely stand. His donkey gave a frightened bray and ran back up the road.

"Tonto!" Pepe called frantically. "Come back!" He turned to chase the donkey, but instead a strong wind caught him. Gasping, he staggered and fell. By the time he had recovered his breath and pulled himself to his feet again, rain had begun to fall in torrents. Now he had no hope of catching Tonto.

Twigs and branches flew through the air. With a boom a great royal palm toppled across the road in front of Pepe. The velocity of the wind was steadily increasing. Above the creaking of the trees and the noise of the pelting raindrops, Pepe could distinguish a continuous rattling sound almost like music. He soon recognized this noise. It was the rattle of millions of seeds in the dry pods of the shaggy-shaggy trees.

After a half-hour of crawling, falling down, and crawling once more, Pepe reached the waterfall. He sat there for a moment, panting.

Shingles, boards, and limbs of trees swished and banged as they sped overhead. The boy knew that he could not stay here. He must follow the water pipe from the brook and reach the shelter of the wall surrounding the López house. The west side of the wall would furnish a barrier against the full force of the buffeting wind.

As Pepe slowly neared the wall, he could hear other sounds above the creaking and grinding of big trees being uprooted and torn apart. His ears caught the mournful howling, braying, and bellowing of the farm animals.

Then he heard another sound. It was the cry of a human being! Pepe continued to follow the water pipe, sometimes on his knees, sometimes on his stomach.

Suddenly he stopped. There in a muddy, soggy heap was Anita López, sobbing pitifully.

"Anita!" Pepe called to her, trying to pitch his voice above the storm.

Anita looked up. "Pepe!" she sobbed. "We—we must get inside!"

They began to crawl toward the house, still following the water pipe. Pepe took the lead, with Anita holding on to one of his feet. At last they reached the protection of the building. Pepe opened the heavy door, and he and the girl staggered inside. There they were greeted by Anita's parents, who were overjoyed to see her unharmed.

Pepe was so exhausted that it was some time before he remembered Tonto and the fruit. Tears sprang to his eyes when he thought of the money he had expected to make. Now he could not buy new shoes, and his old ones were gone.

As Pepe sat drying himself by the kitchen fire, his sad thoughts were interrupted by *Señor* López.

"Pepe," said Anita's father, "today you showed that you are a courageous lad."

"*Muchas gracias*," said Pepe modestly.

"I was wondering," continued *Señor* López, "if you would like a job here. I need a dependable person like you to help drive our truck. While you are going to school, you can work on Saturdays and during vacations. My driver, Carlos, will teach you to drive right away."

Pepe was speechless. He just gulped and nodded at the wonderful proposal.

By the next morning the storm had ceased, and the sun was shining down on the wreckage left by the hurricane. When Pepe started for home, Anita slipped up close and put a small object into his shirt pocket. "Keep it," she whispered.

Not until Pepe had rounded the first curve in the road did he reach into his pocket. Anita had given him her red fountain pen!

The first thing Pepe saw when he arrived home was Tonto munching grass. Pepe's family was safe, too. The house was damaged a little, but surely anyone big enough to drive a truck could repair it.

Pepe walked over to Tonto and whispered into his ear. "Didn't I say that yesterday would be a day to remember? And today is another!"

A Good Bargain

Kimba was sitting on the dusty, sun-baked earth in front of a thatched African hut, listening carefully to the beat of distant drums. To Kimba and his people, drums were a jungle telegraph, passing important messages over great distances from one native village to another.

The boy's face broke into a broad smile as he listened to the good tidings brought by drums. They said the men who wanted to buy crows and crows' eggs had arrived at the district farm school.

Crows were eating up the farm and garden crops of Kimba's people, and a plan had been made to get rid of the pestering birds. A few days ago the village people had been told that some men were coming to the school to gather up as many crows as they could. These men would pay a five-cent coin for a crow's egg and two ten-cent coins for a crow. Now the drums announced that the men had arrived!

Suddenly Kimba had an exciting thought. He was the best nest finder in his tribe, and eggs would be easier to hunt than the hatched birds. He would gather as many eggs as he could and take them to the men at the school. With the money he could buy the village chief a present. It was early morning, but he knew that by afternoon all the boys in the tribe—and maybe the grown-ups, too—would be out hunting crows and crows' eggs. So he did not waste a moment getting started.

Before noon Kimba had a reed basket nearly filled with crows' eggs. Slowly he counted them.

"Twenty-two eggs!" exclaimed Kimba. At five cents apiece he had a fortune! What a present he could get for his chief!

The hot African sun was still high in the sky. There would be time that very afternoon to go with his father, Ohalla, into the city where the farm school was and collect his reward. He hurried home and displayed his treasure-laden basket. To Kimba's delight Ohalla said that he was planning to go to the nearby city right away.

Soon Kimba and his father started out on their journey. In his hand Ohalla carried a long spear as a protection against any hostile animals that

he might meet. On his head he
carried a box of animal figures
that he had whittled out of wood.
Ohalla was a skillful carver and sold his figures to
a shop in the city.

Kimba, too, carried a burden on his head. Balanced on his tight curls was the basket of precious
crows' eggs.

A brisk wind rustled the tall elephant grass along
the path, and a sudden gust set Kimba's basket
rocking on his head. Kimba stopped and held his
breath. What if the wind should upset the basket?
Again the breeze made the basket wobble. Kimba
stopped lest his motion overturn the basket. But
it remained steady, and soon the breeze died down.

An hour later Kimba and his father arrived on the outskirts of the city. After arranging to meet Kimba there later, Ohalla went off toward the shop where he always sold his carvings. Kimba started for the farm school to find the men who wanted to buy the crows' eggs.

Now that he had reached the city with its smooth avenues, so different from the trail, Kimba could run with the basket on his head. So it was not long before he arrived at the farm-school building where the men were to be.

Kimba ran up on the veranda and rapped on the door. A servant appeared and asked the boy what he wanted.

Kimba held out his basket proudly. "The drums have said that the men who will buy crows and their eggs are here. I have brought many such eggs."

"So you have," said the servant, peering into the basket. "But the men who will pay you for the eggs are not here just now. Wait where you are until they return."

"I shall wait," promised Kimba.

The boy sat down on the steps with his basket beside him. Soon he was fast asleep. He slept for almost two hours in the hot rays of the African sun. Probably he would have slept even longer if he had not suddenly become aware of a strange chittering noise.

Kimba stretched his cramped muscles and blinked sleepily. When he looked at his basket, his eyes popped wide open. His eggs! Some were eggs no longer. Some had become baby crows!

At first Kimba thought it was magic. Then he realized what had happened. The hot sun beating down on the eggs for so long had hatched them!

Just then a man approached the house and was greeted at the door by the servant. "That boy," the servant announced, pointing to Kimba, "has some crows' eggs."

"Fine!" said the man. "Let me see how many eggs you have, my lad."

"I have only eight eggs," said Kimba. "See! The good sun has worked magic on the others. They are birds now! And you will pay two ten-cent coins for each bird. Is that not so?"

"Well, yes. Certainly it is true," said the man, rubbing his chin. "But see here, boy! Weren't these all eggs when you brought them here?"

"Yes, but you did not see them then," said Kimba.

The man started to laugh. "I never thought I'd be outbargained by so small a businessman. Now it looks as though I have been!"

Kimba held his breath, hardly daring to believe that he had won the bargain.

"Very well," said the man, still chuckling. "I'll give you the two ten-cent coins for each hatched bird and a five-cent coin for each egg. But mind you, next time I will not pay such a high price for birds unless they are big enough to have feathers."

Kimba, grinning with rapture, said, "Yes, sir! Thank you, sir."

The man began counting so many five- and ten-cent bronze coins into Kimba's two open palms that soon the boy could not hold all the coins. So he put them into his empty egg basket.

To Kimba the coins were an immense fortune. Even after he had bought a present for his chief, there would be money left. He could buy something for his father and for himself, too.

Trotting to the city's edge to meet his father, Kimba began singing in tune with the jingling money in his basket.

Suddenly a big crow flew overhead, cawing loudly. Kimba shouted and waved at the greedy creature. "You have been a plague in the past, you thieving bird. But not today! Today you have done me a good turn. You have made me rich!"

Surprise in Manila

For ten long months Paz Rosario had worked on the satinlike, purple material in a big wooden frame. Skillfully, patiently she was embroidering flowers and leaves and twining branches, using bright-colored threads. With each stitch of her needle went the silent hope of winning the right to attend the 4-H Club Congress to be held in Manila.

At last the young Filipino girl achieved her aim. Her piece of vivid needlework, now made into a skirt, received first prize in the 4-H Club exhibit in the *barrio* where Paz lived. Next the time-and-cost records of her work and color photographs of the embroidery were sent to the judges of the municipality, consisting of several adjoining *barrios*. Again Paz was awarded first place.

Finally her records and pictures were sent to the judges of the province, which included a still larger area of the Philippine Islands. To her delight Paz was chosen to attend the 4-H Congress as a member-delegate from her province. Then the glorious day actually arrived when the journey to Manila was to begin.

Paz paced nervously back and forth outside the door of her country home, waiting for the jeep that was to take her to the boat. "Maybe it's not coming," she thought. "Maybe the meeting has been called off!"

In her hand Paz carried a small suitcase filled with clothes. Among them were the special 4-H uniform she had made and the embroidered skirt that had won her the trip. She had been asked to be on the program at the big banquet of the 4-H Congress. Since the skirt had brought her so much luck, she had decided to wear it for the dance she was going to perform.

Nearby on the ground lay her bundle of rolled bedding. During the Congress the delegates would sleep on cots in a Manila high school. However, they were expected to provide their own bedding.

This would be Paz's first experience in sleeping away from home. But that did not worry her at all.

Nothing worried her except the thought that the jeep might not arrive in time to get her to the boat for Manila.

Suddenly the jeep came into view with an accompanying clatter of pebbles bouncing off the jolting car. Then brakes screeched sharply as the machine pulled up before the anxious girl.

Miss García, the home-demonstration agent who had advised Paz during the 4-H competition, called a welcoming "Hi!"

Immediately Paz began to tremble. Fear, shyness, and excitement filled her mind. But all the uneasiness vanished as her family rushed down the steps of the house to hug her and wish her a wonderful trip.

"Dance well, my daughter," called her mother as Paz ran to the jeep.

After a short ride to the harbor, the week-long boat trip began. There were other 4-H delegates on board. Together the enthusiastic youngsters chatted and made plans for their stay in Manila. Paz spent many hours practicing her dance and thinking about what she would see in the city.

Finally, late one afternoon, the boat docked at Manila. The 4-H delegates and Miss García were driven to the high school where sleeping rooms had been prepared. Many young people were already there. The girls wore green-and-white striped uniforms with 4-H Club emblems on their pockets. The boys were in white, with 4-H emblems on their shirt pockets. They were all talking excitedly to some agricultural and home-demonstration agents.

"How would you like a bus trip around the city after dinner?" asked one of the men.

"Fine!" Paz blurted out. Then she blushed and looked at Miss García shamefacedly.

"Yes, indeed," Miss García agreed with a smile at Paz. "We wouldn't want to miss that."

During the evening there were rumors among the delegates that the President of the Philippines would speak at one of their meetings. Until now Paz had not even dreamed that she might see her country's President. The very possibility made her eyes grow bright. Later, back at the school dormitory, she kept the other girls awake talking about it.

Everyone was up early the next morning. The first session of the 4-H Club Congress was to begin at six-thirty in the beautiful Fiesta Pavilion of the Manila Hotel.

The meeting opened with over two hundred farm boys and girls singing their 4-H song. The faces of the happy youngsters glowed with pride as they recited the 4-H pledge. But while Paz spoke, she kept glancing toward the main door of the room. "Soon the President will come!" she thought.

But she was disappointed. The President did not arrive, although the man who was Secretary of Agriculture did attend the meeting and make a speech.

During the afternoon the young people went on a tour of the factories of Manila. They also visited the magnificent palace of the President. But even there they did not see the important man.

Back at the high school late that afternoon Paz was thoughtful as she brushed her glossy hair and prepared for dinner and the evening entertainment. She admitted to herself that although the day had been exciting, she was disappointed at not having seen the President.

Just then Miss García came into the dormitory. "Are you ready to perform tonight?" she asked.

Paz nodded her head. "I brought my embroidered skirt to dance in," she said. "Will it be all right for me to wear it to the banquet?"

"Of course," said the home-demonstration agent. "I'm sure you'll dance beautifully in it."

Paz thanked Miss García and went to unpack the carefully folded skirt. She gazed at it fondly. "It's lucky I chose clothing for my 4-H project," she thought with a grin. "I could never have brought a calf or a pig or a chicken to Manila."

After dinner Miss Ruiz, supervisor of the home-demonstration agents, made a speech. Then she introduced Paz, the first performer on the program.

Shyly the young girl left her seat at the dinner table and stepped onto the stage of the tremendous room. With a nervous nod at the piano player who was to accompany her, Paz slowly and gracefully began her dance.

For the first few moments Paz was afraid that she would stumble. But as she went through the familiar movements of the dance, she soon forgot her fear. Just as Paz had really begun to enjoy dancing for the audience, she heard the shrill sound of sirens outside the hotel. She noticed that Miss Ruiz, who was presiding, had left her place at the speakers' table and was slipping out of the Fiesta Pavilion through a side door.

A moment later Paz was startled to see everyone in the big audience rise and begin to applaud and cheer enthusiastically. Flushed and pleased, the young girl finished her dance. Then she bowed again and again.

All at once cries of "The President! The President!" filled the air. Only then did Paz realize that the shouts of acclaim were not for her. They were for the man who had entered the pavilion.

Immediately Paz, too, began to clap. Her hands stopped in mid-air when she saw that the President was looking directly at her as he waved a greeting to the crowd.

There was a hushed silence as the man spoke. "I'm sorry that I can stay only a few moments," he told the delegates. "But I am glad that I was able to see even a part of the beautiful dance just performed. Now I should like to hear the 4-H song. Will you sing it—just for me?"

The piano player struck the opening chords, and the delegates began to sing their stirring song. When it was over, the President smiled warmly and left the room amid thundering applause. Not until the sirens announced the departure of the President's car did the delegates quiet down.

As Paz walked to her seat, her thoughts raced happily. "I wanted to go to the 4-H Congress, and I wanted to see the President. But in all the time that I worked on my embroidery, I never dreamed that I would wear the skirt to dance for the President of my country!"

Ring Around the World

Ring around the world
Taking hands together
All across the temperate
And the torrid weather.
Past the royal palm-trees
By the ocean sand
Make a ring around the world
Taking each other's hand;
In the valleys, on the hill,
Over the prairie spaces,
There's a ring around the world
Made of children's friendly faces.

49

Reprinted by permission of the publishers, J. B. Lippincott Company, from *All Through the Year* by Annette Wynne. Copyright, 1932, by Annette Wynne.

I Take a Look at the World

I am ten years old. I live with my mother, my father, my grandfather, and my dog, Danny, in our house right outside North Kansas City, Missouri.

One night when I was nine, the Bauman family was having dinner with us. The Baumans were our next-door neighbors. Mr. Bauman is Ollie; Mrs. Bauman is Rosalie; and Buck is their son, who is my age. They were getting ready to go to Bareilly, India, where Ollie was going to work.

At dinner that night Daddy said, "Why don't you send Buck back to visit us sometime?"

Ollie didn't think much of the idea. So he asked, "Why don't you send Elizabeth over to see us?"

At first Daddy said to Ollie, "You're dreaming." But after a while Daddy agreed that it might be a good idea and said I could go.

That was the real start of the trip I took around the world all by myself.

The first stop on my way to India was Gander, Newfoundland. We weren't supposed to stay long in Gander, but we had to stop there for six hours because the plane had heater trouble. I slept in a room in the airport. The long stop meant that I wouldn't have seven hours in London, and I was a little angry.

When I reached London, some reporters asked a lot of questions. "Weren't you afraid to travel by yourself? How do you like airplanes?" and things like that. One reporter was very nice and bought my dinner for me.

When I got on the plane again, I met Salim, the grandson of the *Nawab* of Rampur. Rampur is forty miles from Bareilly. Salim was nine years old. He was going back to India after fifteen months of school in England. He and I flew together from London to Delhi, in India.

Beirut, in Lebanon, was the first place where I really saw foreign people. At first I thought they were odd. But they aren't. They just seem that way because they can't speak anything but their own language. Of course, I can't speak anything but mine either.

I went shopping in downtown Beirut. The shopping district was much like the one at home, except that this one has the Mediterranean Sea running right next door to the stores.

The plane went to Basra next. Then we flew to the city of Karachi, in Pakistan. After Karachi came Delhi, and the Baumans were at the airport to meet me. It was good to see them. We all stayed with some friends of theirs overnight, and the next day we went to Bareilly by car. It's only 140 miles from Delhi to Bareilly, but it took us almost all day to get there.

The road was bumpy and full of holes, so we had to drive slow. Also, there was only one lane. When a car came from the other way, we pulled off and let it go by unless the people in it let us pass first.

There weren't many cars on the road. There were mostly *tongas* and *rickshas*. A *tonga* is something like a wheelbarrow and is pulled by a horse or a cow. The *ricksha* is pulled by a man on a bicycle.

Bareilly is a very crowded city and is not nearly so modern as Delhi. Many men wear suits like those worn by American men. The Indian women wear *saris*—large pieces of plain or figured cloth wrapped around them a couple of times. Some of the men wear *saris*, too. The postman did. He was barefoot and rode a bicycle. Some of the Indian men wear turbans.

The Baumans lived in a big adobe house with a thatched roof. Nearby they had banana, orange, and coconut trees. The oranges are sour, and the only thing they are good for is orange cake.

I was lucky when I was in Bareilly because Buck was home from school on vacation. His school is about 250 miles from home.

The schoolwork there is harder than it is here. Third-grade work there is like the fourth- and fifth-grade work in my school. In India the pupils study division by two numbers and three numbers in the third grade. At home we do not study it until the fifth grade.

In Bareilly, Buck and I used to wake up around six o'clock in the morning. Breakfast was almost the same as it is at home—eggs, bacon, and toast. For lunch or dinner we often had buffalo steak, which is about like our steak only a little sweeter. Once in a while we had peacock. This tastes a lot like other wild birds, but mostly like wild duck.

The Indian people eat foods that are different from the things we eat. They have *curry* and *chappatti* and *poppars*. *Curry* is a hot, spicy stew. *Chappatti* is a kind of puffy whole-wheat pancake. *Poppars* are like our potato chips, only spicy. Indians also drink buffalo milk and eat buffalo butter. Both the butter and the milk are very white and have a sweet flavor. The Indian people do not believe in killing the buffalo for meat.

The Indians sit either on the floor or on their beds, which they think are very soft even though they are made of rope. I think it would get very tiresome sleeping on rope every night.

During the day Buck and I played in the house, went on hikes, or walked over to the bazaars where most Indians buy all the things they need. These bazaars have shaded booths much like the big market in Kansas City.

Cows wander loose in the streets, and there are a lot of monkeys. Sometimes you see fifty monkeys in the yard eating the pretty flowers. There are also jackals all over, and you don't dare leave your dog out at night because he would be gone in the morning.

I was lucky to be able to visit a real palace while in India. Salim, the boy who flew with me on the plane, invited Rosalie Bauman, Buck, and me to his grandfather's palace at Rampur. The palace is even more beautiful than the ones in fairy tales. It looks like an art museum. It is made of white stone and is very large.

Salim showed Buck and me all around the palace. It has a huge throne room with a crystal throne that has a red velvet covering on the seat. The footstool has the same covering.

I also went into the jungle a few times. It is nearly sixty miles from Bareilly. Ollie and Buck shot a few *chital* and *muntjacs* there. *Chital* is the Indian name for spotted deer, and *muntjacs* are a different kind of deer that bark. Even when they aren't hunted, they don't stay alive very long. Maneating tigers get them before they are even half grown.

In the jungle are a good many trees with vines running up them. There are also palm trees and lots of bamboo. The bamboo grows at least eighty or ninety feet high and is quite dense.

The snakes in the jungle are very dangerous. The most dangerous of all is the cobra. You have to get to a doctor within half an hour if one bites you, or else you don't have much chance of living. The cobra's venom is a deadly poison.

Two days before we went to the jungle, a fierce tiger had killed two men there. So all through our trip Buck and I had to stay close to Ollie and not get separated.

Animals called scorpions are just about as poisonous as a cobra. I had to shake out my pajamas and bedclothes before going to bed. One morning

56

before I woke up, Buck played a trick on me. He put a toy scorpion made of rubber in one of my shoes. I yelled and screamed so loud when I found it that I woke everybody in the house.

I went for a ride on an elephant twice while I was in India. It was even more fun than riding a horse. One day when the Baumans and I were going to Delhi, we passed an elephant. Ollie asked its driver if Buck and I could have a ride. The driver said "Yes."

The elephant kneeled while Buck got up on him. I followed. But I was barely halfway on when the elephant decided that he wanted to stand up. There I was, dangling in air, holding onto the elephant's ear with all my might!

Once I got into the seat, I enjoyed the ride. It was like rocking in a cradle.

Almost before I knew it, the two months were over. It was time to leave India and go home. I had had a good time, and I was sorry to leave.

Buck, Ollie, and Rosalie took me to Delhi, where we said good-by. Then I got on the airplane. I didn't know anyone on the plane, but the pilot and the stewardess were very kind.

The plane stopped in Calcutta and Bangkok for just a very short time. But I was in Hong Kong for about six hours and got to see quite a bit. Hong Kong seems to be a large place. It has a lot of mountains around it. Some of the plane passengers and I rode up the mountains on a train that was open on all sides. We all held on tight.

In Manila I had the first hot dog I had eaten since leaving America. But I didn't like it much. It had too many onions on it and was cooked differently from the ones at home. Next the airplane headed for Guam. I sat up in front flying the plane. Of course, the pilot was helping.

About all we did on Guam was land and take off. We got to Honolulu, Hawaii, on Saturday morning.

I was in Hawaii for three days. My mother's cousin Jane lives there, and I stayed at her house. Almost the first thing we did was to go for a swim in the ocean.

The beach was the prettiest one I'd ever seen because it had palm trees. I think Hawaii looks a lot like Florida, where I once went on a vacation.

Finally I got on the plane that was really going to the United States. We landed in Los Angeles, and there were reporters waiting for me. I spoke on the radio and on television. It was very exciting, but I was more interested in getting home.

I was only in Los Angeles for about four hours. Then I took a plane for Kansas City and got there on a Wednesday afternoon.

When I got back to Kansas City, I had been all the way around the world. On my way to India, I had landed in Newfoundland, England, Turkey, Lebanon, Iraq, Pakistan, and then India.

Two months later on my way home, I had landed at Bangkok, Hong Kong, Manila, Guam, Wake Island, Honolulu, Los Angeles, and finally Kansas City. I had been away from home for two and a half months.

Altogether I traveled 25,000 miles by myself, and the only thing I lost was my small hairbrush. But I didn't really lose that because I know where it is. It's on Guam.

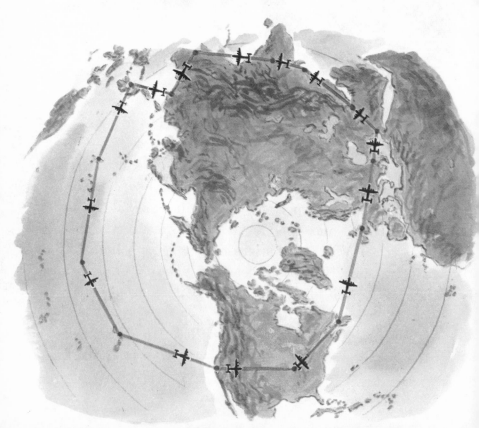

The World
of Nature

Inside the Earth

Climbing a steep cliff was a tiring task on a hot August afternoon. But Philip Huff and his cousin Joe Brian were determined to reach the top. From there they would have a spectacular view of the Ohio River, which flowed along one side of the farm belonging to Philip's father.

Halfway up, the two boys halted and collapsed in a breathless heap. But almost immediately Joe exclaimed, "Say, Phil! Do you feel that air?"

"I certainly do!" Phil agreed, equally surprised by the sensation of cold air blowing on his back.

Curiously the boys glanced around to find the source of the draft. It was Joe who discovered a small crevice in the stony wall of the cliff. As he held a hand against the opening, he felt a current of cool air that obviously came from inside the cliff.

"There must be a cave in there!" Philip cried. "There are several caves in this county, but I've never known of one on our farm."

Though the opening was narrow, the boys were able to enlarge it enough to crawl through. They crept a few feet into the cave and discovered that the roof of the passage was high enough to let them stand erect.

"It's spooky in here," muttered Joe. "This place is like a tomb. I can't see a thing."

"We'd better get a light," Phil suggested. "It's too dangerous to wander around in total darkness."

The boys squeezed out of the hole and scrambled back down the cliff. At the farmhouse Philip got a kerosene lantern, a flashlight, and two big balls of heavy cord.

"What's the string for?" Joe asked.

"We can unwind it as we go through the cave," Philip answered. "Then if our light gives out, we can find our way back by following the cord."

As fast as possible, the two boys returned to the cave. But before they reëntered it, Phil knelt and tied the end of one cord securely around a huge rock outside. He then handed the ball to Joe. After lighting the lantern, Phil led the way through the opening.

Joe, carrying the flashlight and unwinding the ball of string as he went, followed his cousin. Every now and then Joe switched on the flashlight and illuminated the jagged walls of rock.

The boys soon discovered that the meandering passage was leading them deeper and deeper into the earth. At last they found themselves in an enormous chamber that made them gasp in awe.

From the ceiling of the majestic room hung row after row of long, icicle-shaped formations. Between the giant icicles were what looked like delicate lacy curtains. But the boys soon discovered that they were a stonelike substance.

Here and there on the floor were columns that resembled broken tree trunks. In some places these columns reached straight up almost to the roof of the chamber. The spires and columns of stone all glistened like colored gems as rays from the lantern and the flashlight played upon them.

"It's like a great cathedral," murmured Joe.

"Once I read a book about caves," Philip said. "The pictures showed caves just like this one. These long things hanging from the ceiling were formed by dripping water that seeped through cracks in the rocks. They're called stalactites. Some of them look like long icicles and steeples turned upside down."

"What about these things that look like cones growing up from the floor?" Joe asked.

"They were formed by dripping water, too," Phil explained. "In certain caves the water contains dissolved minerals that harden and remain long after the water has evaporated. Drops of dissolved minerals deposited on the same spot for a long time build up columns like the ones we see here. They are called stalagmites."

"It must have taken years and years to build up these stalagmites and stalactites," Joe guessed.

"Thousands of years," Philip declared.

"Come on," urged Joe. "Let's walk on farther. No, wait! My ball of cord is about used up."

"Take this one," Phil replied, pulling the other ball of string from his pocket. "Tie it to the end of your string."

The boys walked across the room, picking their way between the stalagmites. When they reached the other side of the vast chamber, they found another passageway.

"Let's see where this leads," Joe suggested. He walked slowly, moving his flashlight so that the narrow passage was lighted ahead of them. All at once the sound of rushing water was heard. The sound grew into a roar, and the two cousins came suddenly to a small waterfall that flowed out of a fissure in the wall of the cavern. The water splashed down over the rocks and glided away in a little stream.

"An underground brook!" Joe exclaimed. "Let's follow it!"

Cautiously the boys advanced down the passage, tracing the stream's path. Finally Joe and Philip noticed that the passage had widened into another enormous room. Their lights shone on a scene of dazzling brightness.

"A cave of ice!" Philip shouted.

Approaching the wall, the boys found that it did indeed seem to be made of glistening ice. But when Philip touched it, he discovered that it was composed of jutting, cube-shaped crystals.

The boys moved along in front of the wall until Joe cried, "Here are some greenish cubes! They look as if they were made of green ice!"

"They're almost as cold, too," Philip agreed as he touched one. "But they don't melt."

"And look over there!" shouted Joe. "Part of the wall is purplish!"

The boys moved their lights back and forth across the face of the rock wall. The bright beams clearly illuminated tints of green and purple.

"I'm taking a few of the crystals back with me," Joe decided, stuffing some in the pocket of his corduroy trousers. "And I think our exploring will end here. Our second ball of cord is used up."

Winding the string as they went, the two boys retraced their steps to the narrow passage and followed the subterranean stream to the big room with stalactites and stalagmites. At last Phil and Joe saw the distant glimmer of fading daylight. They crawled out through the cave's opening and hurried back to the farm.

Philip's father greeted them worriedly. "Where have you been all this time? I was about to report two lost boys to the sheriff."

"We explored a cave that we found inside the cliff along the river," Phil told him excitedly.

"You boys should know better than to wander around in unexplored caves," Mr. Huff admonished. "You could easily have lost your way."

"Oh, we were careful," Phil informed his father quickly. "We had lights, and we took cord to lead us back."

"And see what we found!" Joe added. He pulled several crystals from a hip pocket and showed them to his uncle.

"Well!" Mr. Huff boomed out. "You boys really did find something! Were there very many of these crystals in the cave?"

"There was one whole wall of them," Phil said. "Why?"

Mr. Huff nodded his head slowly as he examined the cubes. "I think these are fluorite crystals," he explained. "If they are fluorite and if they are plentiful, the cave may prove valuable."

"What's fluorite?" asked Joe.

"Fluorite is a mineral used in producing steel," Mr. Huff said. "It's also used in manufacturing enamelware such as washbasins and bathtubs. In the next county there's a big fluorite mine."

"Boy!" Philip shouted. "Maybe we have a mine of fluorite right here on our farm! Maybe it'll make us rich!"

"That depends on how much of it there is and whether or not it's fluorite," cautioned Mr. Huff.

"How can we find out?" Joe asked excitedly.

"I'll go and see Richard Baldwin this evening. He's an engineer for the fluorite company. I'll show him these crystals and see what he thinks."

The boys could hardly sit still as they waited impatiently for Mr. Huff to return from his trip. When at last he did come back, the two lads rushed to meet him.

"Is it fluorite?" Phil asked breathlessly.

"Is it?" Joe demanded.

"Yes," Mr. Huff answered, nodding happily. "I think I can promise that the fluorite in the cave will give you both a college education a few years from now!"

Penguin Parade

The Royal Zoo in Edinburgh, Scotland, boasts one hundred penguins. Half of them are King penguins. You don't have to be a naturalist or a bird expert to know which is which. All penguins wear the customary white-bosomed dress suit. But in addition, the King wears a necklace—a band of gold feathers about the neck. He is evidently well aware that he has something the other penguins lack, because he saunters along with head held high to show off his "jewelry."

The first of these King penguins, a half dozen, were presented to the Edinburgh zoo many years ago by a whaling company. Now, almost every year, a whaling fleet stops at one of the islands in the antarctic to pick up a few more of the birds. Thus the zoo is kept well stocked.

If you ever spend even a single day in Edinburgh, one thing will always remain a bright and shining memory. You'll never forget the time you saw penguins walking haughtily down the street!

This old Scottish city is the only place in the world, except the antarctic, where penguins run around loose. There are no bars, no leashes. Nothing! Of course, this strange state of affairs is not a twenty-four-hour-a-day thing. But if you're near the zoo between eleven and twelve o'clock any morning, you can see the famous sight.

Edinburgh's Penguin Parade began many years ago, after someone forgot to shut the gate of the birds' wire enclosure. A dozen of the odd little fellows sauntered out of the park and took themselves on a stroll through the city.

They conducted themselves in a splendid manner, and the spectators enjoyed them. So the penguin walk became a regular custom.

The birds themselves really seem to dote on this walk, which they take with their keeper at eleven o'clock sharp every morning. And what a fuss they raise if they are detained by so much as five minutes! They need no clocks to tell them when to start. As it gets closer and closer to the time for their outing, they cluster around the gate and scream for the keeper.

They know their rights and demand them.

When the gate is opened, out they come, eager
to be off on the great adventure.

"Line up there!" says the keeper.   And they do.
They form a column; then off they go through the
zoo grounds and out onto the sidewalk.

You might think that the keeper would have a very hard time controlling his bird charges. But he does not. They are better behaved than many children.

They don't dart into the street, nor do they poke into the things that don't concern them. Occasionally, of course, there is one who "kicks up his heels" to the extent of trotting along at the edge of the curb. The keeper soon puts a stop to this antic with a nudge and a brief scolding.

The daily walk covers more than a mile. These polar natives are not built for speed, and the trip generally lasts about an hour.

Although this odd event has been taking place for years, people never tire of seeing it. Travelers passing through Edinburgh blink, shake their heads in disbelief, and stop their cars to witness the strange spectacle. As a result, there is always a line of halted cars along the entire course of the penguins' extraordinary march.

People may find it hard to get used to the idea of penguins walking loose around the city, but the penguins seem to accept it casually. Although they take the same route every day, they never fail to find something that interests them. But, like well-mannered ladies and gentlemen, they never touch the subject of their curiosity. They only cluster about and look at it. Turning their heads from side

to side, they study the strange
object from every angle. Their
curiosity at last being satisfied,
they resume their walk.

Human beings think of Edinburgh's penguins as
very interesting people. The penguins, in turn,
accept people as the oddest birds. Whenever people
visit them at the zoo, the penguins stand for hours
in one spot with their heads cocked to one side,
eying the visitors. The birds seem eager to know
and remember each one.

So if you are ever in the British Isles, by all
means get to Edinburgh. For you will always
remember the day you saw the Penguin Parade!

Enchanted Island

Douglas Spencer was standing on the deck of the *Falcon*. As he watched Captain Jensen bring the sailing vessel into Academy Bay, Douglas' father told him the exciting news. "While I hunt here for those rare fish I'm to get for the San Francisco aquarium, you and your cousin Randall will have a chance to explore Indefatigable Island. It's said to be enchanted, you know."

All during their ocean trip Randall had talked of the museum specimens he hoped to collect when they reached the Galápagos Islands. Douglas had listened enviously—and now he was going exploring with his scientist cousin!

Early the next morning the boys carefully loaded the rowboat with provisions and sufficient water for a five-day camping trip. Then they set out from the *Falcon* for Indefatigable, a half mile away.

A short time later Randall and Douglas rowed up to the island and made the boat fast to the stout

Adapted from *Treasure of the Tortoise Islands* by Victor W. Von Hagen and Quail Hawkins. Copyright, 1940, by Harcourt, Brace and Company, Inc.

pier. A friendly fisherman offered them rooms in his home and helped transfer their things.

"I'll have a quick look around," Randall said when everything had been brought ashore. He went out, leaving Doug to put away their things.

His task finished, the boy sat down to await his cousin's return. One hour passed—then two—and still no Randall. Douglas became tired of waiting. He put into a knapsack the lunch he had brought from the ship, his first-aid kit, and some matches. He attached a sheath knife, his Scout hatchet, and a canteen of water to his belt. After scribbling a note to his cousin, he flung the knapsack over his shoulder and set off along the deserted beach.

It was an hour later when Randall found the note.

> Couldn't wait any longer. Have gone for a
> hike. Think I'll take a look at the wreck
> we passed on way here. Back soon—Doug.

Knowing how dangerous it was to wander alone on these islands, Randall was alarmed. He should not have stayed away so long, since he was responsible for his cousin. He made sure his canteen was full and set out in the direction of the beach.

Douglas, meanwhile, was keeping close to the shore as he tried to locate the old wreck. It could not be far, he thought. It had seemed only a few minutes from the time he had first seen it until the *Falcon* had moved into Academy Bay.

"What crazy-looking plants there are here!" he thought, squinting at a giant cactus growing out of the lava. Apparently these plants did not need soil. They were flourishing on bare rock.

Balancing himself for just a moment before jumping across a crevice, Doug thought that there really was nothing enchanting about this island. He had read stories about people being shipwrecked on a desert island. But he had imagined an island with waving palms and plenty of coconuts to eat and a rippling stream of water. This island was a barren place. He was glad that he was just on a hike and would get back for dinner.

While picking his way gingerly along the rough lava, he suddenly saw a large iguana rise up in front of him. The animal appeared so abruptly that it seemed to have sprung out of the rock it was on.

Not only the suddenness of the lizard's appearance but its immense size as well had startled Douglas. The iguana was almost four feet long from the tip of its nose to the end of its tail. Its whole length was made ferocious looking by a series of spines that ran like a dragon's mane along the back. The thick, heavy body was spotted with daubs of green, black, and orange. The big scaly feet ended in five fingers, giving the appearance of a monster's hands.

Douglas stared, his mouth open with surprise. The iguana faced the trespasser on the protruding shelf of lava rock and gave him a fierce glare. Poised and unmoving, it studied the boy attentively. Then its great head began to shake up and down. Its mouth opened to show rows of sharp teeth resembling bits of white coral.

The boy pulled out his Scout hatchet and held it tightly in his hand. Into his mind sprang a tale he had read of explorers discovering a lost world still inhabited by dinosaurs. That was what he felt he was—someone in a lost world suddenly faced with a dinosaur or dragon. Yet he knew that this was only a lizard. Stepping forward cautiously, he kept watching the iguana, ready to defend himself if necessary.

As the boy moved, the big iguana ran quickly to the water and plunged in. The waves broke over the black lava, making it as shiny as wet coal. A short way out from the shore were rocks covered with seaweed. Suddenly the iguana came to the surface of the water and swam toward the rocks. Its feet were held close to its body; but its long tail moved strongly from side to side, propelling the animal through the water. Aided by its claws, the iguana climbed onto the weed-covered rocks. After resting a moment, it began to eat.

When Douglas saw the ferocious-looking animal calmly munching seaweed, he laughed. Scared of a vegetarian lizard!

His momentary fright over, Douglas stood there watching the creature devour the seaweed. Waves occasionally rose over the rocks, and he expected to see the iguana washed off. But it did not budge. After each wave it was still there, holding on tightly and eating.

In a few minutes Doug went on. He climbed around the side of a hill that extended to the sea and came upon hundreds of iguanas basking in the sun. Some were all black. Some had spots of different shapes, colors, and sizes. As the boy approached, the lizards started for the sea.

Encouraged by his success with the lone iguana, Douglas went toward them. They scattered like leaves blown over the ground. Some of them took refuge in the crannies of the rocks to escape this two-footed creature who pursued them. Douglas noticed that the smaller ones refused to enter the water, though the larger ones did not mind it.

After driving off the iguanas, Douglas became aware that his feet had begun to hurt from walking on the sharp, rough lava. He could feel through his shoes the hard edges of the rocks.

He sat down to rest a moment. As he sat, he heard a snorting and scraping. The sound seemed to come from the other side of the rock on which he was resting.

Douglas turned and peered around anxiously. In a level spot between the rocks, two great crested male iguanas were locked in combat. They lay close to the ground with their heads pushed together. The spikes on their heads meshed like the gears of a machine. Thus locked, they were shoving each other back and forth.

Farther away, watching from a pile of rocks that overlooked the arena, a bevy of smaller iguanas stared at the two contestants. Douglas wondered what the outcome would be. Would they fight to the death? Apparently not, for time was called occasionally. Then the iguanas would draw back from the battle to wipe their noses on some rocks. They had pushed each other so hard that blood was flowing from their nostrils as well as from their mouths.

Separated, they would move their heads up and down and open their mouths savagely. Then they would advance toward each other again, nodding and snorting, until once more they were belaboring each other. Since the struggle showed no signs of ending, Douglas decided to go on.

He walked alongshore, looking for the wreck; but new sights constantly arrested his attention. It was past noon when he decided that he was hungry. He reached into his knapsack and took out sandwiches and cookies. When he had finished eating, he drank freely from his canteen.

"I guess I shouldn't drink so much," he told himself. "But I'll be back at the harbor soon. We have water there." He took another big swallow.

While he sat looking out over the sea, he decided that it would be nice to soak his smarting feet. He walked carefully over the sharp stones to a little beach of white sand. Sitting on a rock, he pulled off his shoes and dangled his feet in the water. As he gazed out over the Pacific, he noticed that the blue sky and water were almost the same color. The entire seascape seemed forsaken and quiet. But the scene on the beach was different.

Whole platoons of red crabs ran along the shore, their bodies as big around as saucers. Like the iguanas, they were sunning themselves. Some were walking alongshore, feeding on the jetsam of the

beach. Their tireless pincers were constantly going up and down as they reached into the sand and brought things up to their mouths.

When one crab bumped another, a fight began. Holding their pincers in front of their bodies and using them as if they were boxing gloves, the crabs sparred back and forth. One would swing out and crash his pincer against the other's head. Back would come the pincer of the other. Finally one crab lost a pincer. It lay in the sand, opening and closing even though it no longer had any contact with its owner. The creature that had lost its pincer left the fight and scurried toward the sea.

Suddenly the crabs stopped their cavorting. It seemed as if they had all been enchanted and turned to stone. Some of them held their pincers in midair. Then their telescopic eyes rose to full height, and the creatures began to retreat.

"What is happening?" wondered Douglas. "They must be afraid of something."

Just then, around the corner of a rock stalked a small, powder-blue heron. About ten inches high and armed with a long stiletto-like beak, it moved slowly toward a crab. At last the bird sprang— and missed. Before it could turn again, its prey had dashed for safety, slipping between the rocks.

The heron ran up to the rocks and pecked angrily at the crab. But the crab flattened out and backed farther into the crevice. With no hope of capturing that meal, the heron turned on the other crabs. All retreated in good order, without hurry. Little by little they moved toward the rocks away from the beach. Every forward move by the heron brought a backward move by the crabs. Again the heron singled out a retreating crab for special attention and began to stalk it.

Slowly the eight legs of the crab felt for a foothold on the lava rocks. The heron poised and flew at it. Equally agile, the crab leaped backward into the rocks. Again outwitted, the heron raised its crest in anger and flew off down the beach. Free of their enemy, the crabs came slowly out of hiding and resumed their fierce play.

Douglas put on his shoes and started off again along the shore. Here the rocks were larger and their surfaces sharper. The toes of Doug's canvas shoes were soon cut as if by a jagged instrument. In full glare of the sun the island had become very quiet.

Everything seemed more parched than it had been that morning. Two black finches, looking like English sparrows with big beaks, were struggling over a pad of cactus, trying to squeeze out a few drops of moisture.

Painfully Douglas began the ascent of a tall mound of rock from which he could survey the surface of the island. A short distance from the lava-rock coast he saw a sandy area where the cactus began. Beyond the cactus plants was a slight rise of ground with some small trees.

About a half mile inland Douglas saw a large lagoon. He made his way toward it, believing that he might find some softer earth on which walking would be less painful. He began to wonder how much farther he had to go to find the wreck.

Approaching the lagoon, the boy noticed sandy soil around its edge. The trees, although not high, did afford a little shade. As he hiked along, each step cushioned in deep soil, Douglas gave a sigh of relief. The walking was certainly much better. But soon he noted that the vegetation had a curious sameness. The landscape had no large juts of rock or groups of trees by which he might find his way.

Halfway around the lagoon Douglas saw some big birds wading in the water. At his approach the birds broke into a quick walk, next into a run, and then were off in flight. After flying around the lagoon a few times, they settled down near the edge again. Moving up very cautiously, Doug parted the plants that lined the shore and peered through. He saw that the big birds had gathered close to some mounds that were apparently made of mud.

Doug readily identified the birds as flamingos. There was no mistaking them, for he had seen many pictures of flamingos. They were about three or four feet high, with pink and white feathers and curious beaks. Their long necks stretched down to the water as the birds searched for food.

Looking again at the mounds, the boy could hardly believe his eyes. In the center of each was a single egg. But not a mother was on her nest!

"Those eggs will get cold," the boy thought.

The pink birds walked slowly as if they sensed some danger. One flamingo approached her nest and put a webbed foot on the rim of the mound, which rose about twelve inches from the ground. She shook her other foot as if to free it from water and dirt. Then the bird posed for a moment on the rim like a diver about to make a backward dive. All at once she plumped down on the egg. Doug wondered how the egg could possibly stand such rough treatment.

Suddenly the flamingo gave a start and left the nest. She turned the egg over with her beak and tapped it sharply.

"What in the world can that bird be doing?" Douglas muttered as the flamingo tapped the egg again and broke a bit off. He watched carefully while the mother bird broke off another piece.

From within the egg came a faint chirping as the shell cracked still more from the contortions of the baby bird inside.

The mother stepped back, watching. She strutted up and down before the other flamingos, who were now sitting on their eggs. "There, old long-necks," she might have been saying. "My little one is coming out first."

The others were jealous, Douglas decided. They pecked at the proud mother when she came too near.

Now the small flamingo began to break out of the egg, assisted by its mother's beak. Finally the baby gave a harder shake, and the last of the shell came off.

"Well, you got out of that!" Douglas said aloud. His voice startled the birds. With a great cackling and fussing they left their nests.

"I must have been sitting a long time watching those birds," the boy decided. He looked at the sun. It was sinking, and realization of his plight came to him.

He knew that in the tropics it grew dark very quickly—almost directly after sunset. He must hurry to get back to the harbor before night.

Douglas began to retrace his steps. Suddenly he knew that he was not sure which way he had come. If only he had brought a compass! Then he realized that he could never cross those crevices that split the rocks except by daylight. At this thought he grew panicky. Fear gripped him; a cold shiver raced down his back, spreading throughout his body. What a fool he had been!

Realizing the necessity for calmness, he began to talk aloud. "What have you to be afraid of?" he admonished himself sternly. "There are only lizards and birds here. Remember what Father says —people get lost only if they get panic-stricken. If I can't make it back to the fisherman's house to-night, I can get back sometime tomorrow morning."

He felt better at that and began to gather wood to build a fire. He gathered a great deal of it, for the night would surely be chilly. Already it was cooler. The sun had disappeared, and its last faint rays barely lighted the sky. Things became gray and indistinct.

The dull roar of the sea came to Doug's ears as the fire leaped and crackled. Reaching into his knapsack, he took out a biscuit and the piece of chocolate saved from lunch. He wondered how much water he had. Raising the canteen, he swallowed what was left. Now he regretted that he had had so much at lunch.

The fire made things seem more cheerful; but as the daylight faded, the shadows from the flames took on weird, flickering shapes. Douglas drew closer to the blaze. He was no longer a bold explorer. He was just a tired, frightened boy.

Sitting huddled beside the fire, he tried not to listen to the strange night noises. Above the roaring of the sea he thought he heard animals moving about. Once or twice he seemed to hear voices. But when he called, there was no reply. Finally he was positive that he heard shuffling, uncertain footsteps in the dark. He took out his hatchet, gripping it tightly. Yes, he did hear steps. Someone was stumbling through the brush.

He raised himself, ready for he knew not what.

"Doug—are you all right?"

"Randall!" Douglas shouted, going to meet him.

"Are you all right, Doug? What happened?"

"I was interested in things and forgot the time. Then the sun went down so fast that I couldn't get back before dark," blurted Doug all in one breath.

"There's no sense trying to get back tonight," Randall advised. "It's too dangerous walking in the dark. We might as well stay by the fire and try to get some sleep."

Douglas agreed and began to relate the day's events. Long before he had finished, he had fallen asleep. His first day of exploration was over.

The Wolf

When the pale moon hides and the wild wind wails,
And over the treetops the nighthawk sails,
The gray wolf sits on the world's far rim,
And howls: and it seems to comfort him.

The wolf is a lonely soul, you see,
No beast in the wood, nor bird in the tree,
But shuns his path; in the windy gloom
They give him plenty, and plenty of room.

So he sits with his long, lean face to the sky
Watching the ragged clouds go by.
There in the night, alone, apart,
Singing the song of his lone, wild heart.

Far away, on the world's dark rim
He howls, and it seems to comfort him.

"The Wolf" by Georgia R. Durston, reprinted by permission of the
Child Training Association, Inc.

Orphan of the Wilderness

The big moon poked up through the trees along the backwash of Tom Henton's dam, its golden face reflected in the still waters. The moon was enormous. As it rose, the landscape took on pale colors—gray and silver, lavender and faint green. Soon the splendid shining paled the stars.

A group of teal stirred in the growing brightness. On a high, bare tree a heron changed from one leg to the other. Innumerable elephant moths in search of honey became gray, darting, velvet blurs instead of unseen, humming, brushing bodies. The faint scent of thin-petaled white spider lilies all along the waterway filled the Australian night like an invisible flood.

Presently, down a little dusty path through the bleached silver grass came a family of kangaroos.

92

Moving with tranquil undulation upon hoppers and hands, they came to the water.

The "old man" of the mob was first—an immense red warrior, velvet-furred in pale chestnut across back and legs, tawny cream on his chest and belly. Weighing three hundred pounds, he stood seven feet when he rose upright on toes and tail to face an enemy. Sixteen wives and several small, fat joeys followed. The does were much smaller than their lord. With the exception of one who was blue, all had fur of a brownish mouse color. Their ears were large and quivering. Their eyes were dark, deerlike, and sad. Yet actually they were very happy creatures.

Seeking for shoots or seeds beside the path, they chittered conversationally. With tiny dark hands they caught at each other's heavy, muscular tails that dragged in the dust. Soon they came out on the sod by the dam and nibbled the tender green grass.

It was here that Chut took his first good look at the world. He had lived in his mother's pouch for a long time. There he had changed from the size of a newborn mouse to a ten-pound creature of exquisite loveliness. He was gentle, velvety, and trembling-eared, with huge dark eyes and dainty, dark, clutching hands. Tonight for the first time he was dissatisfied with the warmth and security of the pouch. His legs with their two well-polished black toenails rebelled at being neatly tucked above his head.

"Chut!" he called out sharply. "Chut! Chut! Chut!"

His mother, the little blue doe, answered with a disapproving "Ch-ch!" and shut her pouch.

But Chut had glimpsed a new world of magic brightness and keen new scents. He wanted to get out. He kicked. He clawed. He made strange commotions beneath his mother's ivory pinafore until she opened her pouch and spoke sternly to him. Chut just reached up and caught her nose, touching his to it as if with a kiss. Then the doe tucked her hands around him, lifted him out, and set him down.

He staggered clumsily, the moonlight glinting on the cowlick in the middle of his plump back and shining faintly through his pinkish-coral ears. He clutched at his mother as he tried to steady himself upon his slender hoppers. He wobbled and fell with his legs sticking up absurdly.

In this position the little joey felt more secure. In a moment he grasped at one of his hoppers as a baby might at its foot. He stretched out to his full length and grasped his toes again, looking all about him with bright, knowing eyes.

Had his mother been older, she would never have let him out while he was so little. But she was a very young doe, and he was her first baby. She sat up to her full height and snatched playfully at a passing elephant moth. Then she, too, lay down and rolled in the sand and across the short, fragrant rug of green. Another doe came and rolled beside her. They grappled, turning and twisting like two playful children. They leaped up and played tag through the trees.

Suddenly a shot rang out. Chut was quickly thrust into his mother's pouch, and the mob was off, thirty feet at a bound. There was another loud sound like the first. Chut's mother fell but soon was up and off again. The joey could feel the

95

desperate surge of her leaps. Then as the strange sounds finally died away, the blue doe lifted him out of her pouch. With a lurch she fell to the ground. Chut was frightened. He did not know what had happened. He wanted to get back into the safe pouch, but somehow he sensed that he never would. He sat up, holding his little hands as a dog does when it begs. He chittered with all the energy of his baby voice. Then he slept, holding to the fur of his dead mother.

He woke with an overwhelming shock of panic. The daylight was blinding him. As he sat there unhappy and shelterless, the shadow of an eagle swept across him. The bird changed its course, poised, and then came hurtling toward the furred baby in the grass. It clutched at Chut and left a knifelike cut across the brownish fur. Missing its hold, it rocketed up again.

Chut fled wobblingly. The grass tripped him. Sharp leaf edges cut his back and legs. Twigs poked him in his furry stomach. He jumped at shadows and twittered with fear at the sound of the wind. His sides were pinched with thirst; his fur was draggled. But he stumbled on, making tiny hopper marks in the dust as he went.

Then he came to a worn dusty path. It smelled of kangaroos! Instinct told him that it led back to the dam. Chut hurried there.

At the dam Chut did not know what to do. He was very thirsty. But he had never had anything except milk, which he had always taken lying flat on his back in his mother's pouch.

Instinct told him that the water might soothe the torture of his thirst, but he had not learned to stoop and drink. Instead, after a careful look about, he placed his little hands on the sod, lowered his head between them, and turned a somersault. On his back he reached up his hands, but no drink awaited them. He called. There was only silence. At last he crept away into the shadows.

The day wore on through the long afternoon. Dusk had come when a voice close by called, "A joey!" Then a beam of light flashed into the eyes of the trembling baby.

In an instant Chut was surrounded by some men. Tom Henton, who had found Chut, seemed pleased.

"He's a little beauty," said Tom. "I'm going to take him home to my wife." He held Chut up by the scruff of the neck and poked him with a finger. "He has a lot of nasty scratches, poor little nipper! I guess he belongs to that dead doe we found this afternoon."

The other men pressed around. "The joey needs food," said one.

Gathering up their things, they moved on. Chut hung limp and helpless under his captor's arm.

At the camp back over a ridge there was discussion as to how the baby should be fed. One man said, "He won't drink unless he's upside down." So they got a pair of trousers, tied a knot in one leg, and hung the trousers on a tree by the back strap. Then they held Chut up before it. He looked at it as if he were puzzled.

"Better let him get in himself," said Tom, and he gave Chut a push. It worked. Instinctively Chut grasped the top of the trousers and lowered his head. Bracing his hoppers against the man's stomach, he turned an expert somersault into the depths of the leg.

Once again he was swinging as a little kangaroo should swing. He was enclosed, safe. He gave a feeble chitter.

One of the men stepped forward with a rubber tube stuck into a tin of milk. Gently he offered the tube to the hungry joey.

Chut sucked on the tube. Milk came up into his mouth! He made swift little ticking sounds of happiness; and still drinking, he fell asleep in the warm embrace of the trouser leg.

As Chut's wounds healed, he learned many new things. He learned the smells of fire and tobacco smoke and the smell of men. He knew the mellow smell of coffee, the odors of frying bacon, broiling chops, and potatoes roasting in ashes. He learned about the sneeziness of flour and the sharp tang of tea. He found out that fire was hot and that kerosene was nasty.

His ears became accustomed to queer new sounds. Soon the clatter of kettles, loud laughter, and the clanging music of horse bells ceased to frighten the little joey.

After a month's work on the farthest part of the great ranch, Tom Henton returned to his home. Chut went with him—swinging securely in one leg of the old trousers attached to the man's saddle. Only when the horse's trotting caused Chut to bounce did he chitter in protest.

Arriving at the homestead, Tom Henton was met by his young wife.

"I've brought you a baby kangaroo," Tom said.

He untied the old trousers from the pommel of the saddle and held them out to Mrs. Henton.

She took the bulging garment hesitatingly as her husband dismounted and stood beside her.

"Oh, the darling!" she cried. "He's so little! So soft! What shall we call him?"

"Chut! Chut! Chut-ch-ch-ch!" cried the joey.

So he was called Chut. During the day he followed Mrs. Henton about like a little dog. He still slept in the trousers, which swung from a tree. This garment was always called "Chut's pants."

At the homestead there was soft green grass in which to roll and pepper trees beneath which to play. Chut found it a quite satisfactory world in which to grow up.

A Prayer for Little Things

Please God, take care of little things,
The fledglings that have not their wings,
Till they are big enough to fly
And stretch their wings across the sky.

And please take care of little seeds,
So small among the forest weeds,
Till they have grown as tall as trees
With leafy boughs, take care of these.

And please take care of drops of rain
Like beads upon a broken chain,
Till in some river in the sun
The many silver drops are one.

Take care of small new lambs that bleat,
Small foals that totter on their feet,
And all small creatures ever known
Till they are strong to stand alone.

And please take care of children who
Kneel down at night to pray to you,
Oh, please keep safe the little prayer
That like the big ones asks your care.

"A Prayer for Little Things" by Eleanor Farjeon, copyright, 1945, by Houghton Mifflin Company, is reprinted by permission of and arrangement with Houghton Mifflin Company, the authorized publishers. World rights outside the U.S. from A. Watkins, Inc., New York.

Biggest Wild Animal Business

Do you want to buy a baby gorilla, a leopard, or a thirty-foot python? Or a rare talking bird? Or any kind of pet from a mouse to an elephant? Then there is a bird-and-animal company in New York City that is the place for you.

The owner of the company sells countless dogs, cats, tropical fish, birds, and other varieties of household pets. However, he is not an ordinary pet dealer. He is the biggest importer of wild animals in the country.

Before he can bring any animal to the United States, it must be quarantined for one month in its native country in a mosquito-proof building. This quarantine is to make certain that the animal is free from disease.

When the animals are proved healthy, they are ready for shipment. One of the company's many foreign agents will be on hand to supervise the loading aboard ship and to accompany the cargo to New York.

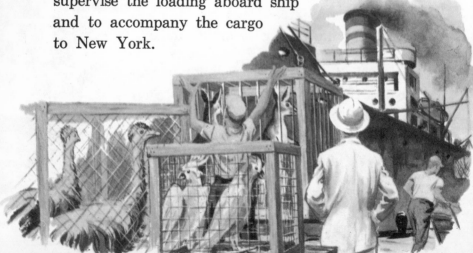

"If we don't have a certain animal in stock, we can get it!" is the advertisement of the company. When a zoo or circus places an order for an animal not in stock, a company agent in India, Africa, or South America is telegraphed. The agent will try to buy the animal from a native animal dealer. But sometimes a trapping expedition is necessary to obtain the particular animal ordered.

One of the most daring agents is "Jungle Jenny." Her job as nursemaid in charge of animal cargoes has put her in many dangerous situations. Once during a thirty-six-day voyage she was in charge of a large shipment of wild animals.

"Early one morning," Jungle Jenny relates, "I went down into the ship's hold with two members of the crew to water the usually sluggish pythons. I raised the lid of the cage slowly and got the shock of my life. One of the huge pythons had pushed up against a steel bar of the cage and bent it. Out he came like a flash!

"He was thirty-two feet long and weighed one hundred seventy-five pounds. Recklessly I grabbed the python below the head and tried to pin it down. The snake coiled its body around me and started to constrict. I screamed, and the two men seized the python's tail. They held him down so that he could not coil again. When I finally got the snake back into the cage, I was shaking like a leaf."

One morning at the New York dealer's shop, a young chimpanzee named Bozo escaped from his cage before the shop was opened. He climbed into the display window. There he found a kitten in a box with its mother.

Reaching into the box, Bozo took out the kitten, pushed back the mother cat, and closed the lid. He then began to play with the kitten. Soon scores of people gathered outside the store window to stare at the unusual scene.

After a while the kitten got tired and went to sleep. Bozo, eager to keep on playing, prodded the kitten. At this, a woman spectator screamed. She rushed off to telephone the police that a monkey was killing all the animals in the pet shop. Six police officers hurried to the shop with drawn guns.

Shortly afterwards the animal dealer arrived. He had a hard time convincing the police that Bozo meant no harm and only wanted to play.

On another occasion one of the dealer's assistants entered the outer door of a large cage containing one hundred monkeys. He was trying to rescue a baby monkey whose foot was caught in a wire netting. When the man found it necessary to open an inner door, he neglected to close the outer one.

Without any warning the handler was knocked flat by an avalanche of monkeys. They rushed over him to an open window and ran up a fire escape.

For six hours afterwards the downtown business section was in an uproar. Monkeys climbed over roofs and down fire escapes. The aggressive little fellows invaded shops and restaurants. Traffic was completely blocked by hundreds of spectators. Gleefully they watched the antics of the monkeys and the recapture of the mischievous creatures.

Because of the great expense of obtaining and caring for zoo and circus animals, the dealer's prices are high. Prices of animals usually range from twenty-five dollars for a common monkey to twenty thousand dollars for a rare *okapi* or a *bongo*. The *okapi* is a purplish-brown, short-necked relative of the giraffe. The *bongo* is a reddish-striped forest antelope.

The next time you go to the zoo or circus, try to remember how difficult and dangerous it is to capture the animals that you are staring at. Also give some thought to the men and women who have given their time, and often their lives, to make our circuses and zoos the fascinating places they are.

The Shining Gateway

At last after heavy rains Willow Creek began to clear, and Flash was venturing home. The big rainbow trout had left the river at dusk on the day before. Now with six miles of winding creek behind him, he lay at sunrise in a reach of water just below a deep pool. The pool was the feeding place where for many summers Flash had been the undisputed ruler.

But a tragic change had come to Willow Creek. No longer did clear, cold water seep into it from feeder streams through miles of forest floor. The big trees had been felled and the undergrowth cut.

Improper logging methods had caused erosion of the soil, and after every rain the water was charged with silt. Forest fires had done all the rest of the damage. Many of the creek's rainbow and cutthroat trout had been driven out. Others had been stranded when the water level of the blighted stream had suddenly dropped.

Uncontrolled spring floods had destroyed the eggs and fry of the surviving fish, but the silver-flanked Flash always returned to Willow Creek. For in spite of the tragic changes that had taken place along the miles of his underwater kingdom, Flash had never failed to find food in the pool below the falls.

The light breeze of that June morning touched the leaves of overhanging willows, and golden sunlight speckled the smooth water above the big trout. A caterpillar, shaken from a twig by the breeze, fell on the surface with a soft plop. There was a sudden swirl, and an instant later Flash nosed into the coiling eddy. The shimmer of his closing gill covers showed that the tasty bite had not been missed.

At the head of the reach a moth was whirling on the surface with draggled wings. A quick tail thrust, and the rainbow trout shot ahead to snatch the insect under. Only for a moment did Flash linger here. Then surging grandly up the ripple, he pressed on, for the call of the home pool was strong upon him. Something seemed to tell the giant trout that there would be abundant feeding in his old haunt—the falls pool.

That morning Ron Lincoln left the ranch house and hurried toward the falls. Ron was anxious. This was the fifth day since the freshet; and Flash, the trout he had fed for two summers, had not returned. Stopping where black ants swarmed on a stump, he broke off the rotted wood and scooped out a handful of the plump egg-clusters. These he dropped into the rusty tin can he carried.

Ron walked stealthily as he neared the creek. Below the stony ledge over which swift water churned, he crouched behind a screen of willows bordering the bank. He tossed the ant eggs upstream. Turning quickly, he lifted a trap door in the ground and eased himself down into a pit no wider than the packing case that lined it.

He reached up and slid the door into place so that no light from above came into this observation post that he had devised. Ron had set a sheet of glass in a wall of concrete against the riverbank. Beyond this glass he could watch the stream's pebbled bottom fade into shimmering shadows.

Then against the window a silvery picture sprang to sudden life. Out of the bubbles upstream, Ron saw the first clump of ant eggs come drifting past.

A few yearling trout drove at them, one darting against the window in its eagerness. As a large school of salmon fingerlings rushed in, a savage squawfish shot forward and tried to seize one. But Flash, the splendid trout that Ron loved to watch, did not appear.

During the low water of late winter when Ron had built his marine studio, he had thought of it chiefly as a hobby. Gradually the strange beauty of this underwater world had gripped him, for Ron seemed to have been born with a love of wild things in his heart. His simple marine studio, copied from a picture of a tropical aquarium, had come to be a shining gateway to adventure. Here the boy's keen, exploring mind had led him to glimpse a new and exciting world.

While crouching at the window, Ron suddenly lifted his head. From somewhere he heard a muffled shout. He pushed back the trap door and looked all around. Coming toward him was his brother, Wilbur. He had Ron's box camera under his arm.

Pulling a newspaper from the pocket of his over-alls, Wilbur thrust it at Ron.

"Talk about luck!" he cried. "As soon as I read this, I came on the run. The Tourist Bureau in town is giving fifty dollars for the best—— But here, you read it!"

Ron scanned the interesting announcement in the newspaper that Wilbur had brought.

DO YOU LIKE WILDLIFE?

As a part of our advertising program, we are offering fifty dollars for the best wildlife photograph taken within twenty miles of River City. All the photographs must be clear and unusually interesting.

Professor Donald Orville Howard, a well-known conservationist and scientist at Dayton College, will be the judge. The contest closes at noon on Saturday, June 9.

Fifty dollars! That, with money from other jobs, would pay his room and board for one term at the college where Ron meant to go someday. It would mean the start of a course in science to prepare for the career as a naturalist that he longed for.

"Old Flash's picture will win the prize money easily," Wilbur rejoiced. "Why, what's wrong?" he demanded, looking at his brother's gloomy face.

"I'm afraid Flash is gone for good," answered Ron. "Last time the creek silted up he was back in three days. But now it's been five days and——"

At that instant the sound of a mighty splash came through the willows. Ron grabbed the camera, and his sun-bleached hair vanished down the pit like a startled gopher diving into its hole.

"I see Flash! He's come back!" Ron shouted as the lid dropped over his head.

He knew nothing of underwater photography. But during the next two hours the shutter on his camera clicked each time the great rainbow drifted near the glass. The perfect streamlining of this superb fish was beautiful to see. To Ron, with his eager curiosity about wildlife, what he was observing was more thrilling than any motion picture ever filmed. His long period of watchful waiting was at last being richly rewarded.

Old Flash had come back hungry from the river. While squawfish might have feasted on the small trout that inhabited the falls pool, this speckled aristocrat was different. He would feed only in the swift current that swirled past the observation window.

Thousands of clumsy flying ants were swarming across the meadow that morning. Hundreds of them had fallen into the upper reaches of the creek and were being carried downstream. When one of the drifting ants showed through the cloudy bubbles below the falls, Flash drove at it swiftly and with a confidence that was exciting to watch.

Once a big squawfish, attracted by the rich feeding, tried to poach on Flash's territory. But as the poacher came swimming along the bottom, the trout took after it like an angry pup, battering its flabby flanks with open jaws and driving it off.

Ron snapped picture after picture until all the film on the roll had been exposed. It was nearly noon when he straightened out his cramped legs and pushed back the trap door. In the pit his eyes had grown used to dim light, and he was surprised to see that a haze had actually dimmed the sunlight.

"I hope we aren't going to have bad weather," Ron thought as he hurried home. At the house he wrapped his film for the mailman to take to town, where it would be developed.

"It's lucky you got those pictures while it was bright," said Wilbur. "Do you think they'll turn out all right?"

"Hope so," Ron replied. "It'll be late Monday before the developed prints can get back from town. If they're not good, maybe I can take better ones next week."

But bad weather broke. On Monday when Ron came home from high school, Willow Creek was coming into freshet. Later he saw the prints that had come by mail and learned the worst. To his humiliation four of the negatives were complete blanks. In the other four, Flash barely showed through the gray fog of underexposure.

There was no time to lose. Silt was starting to cloud the water, and by morning Flash would be driven downstream. It would be days before he came back. Ron had to get a good picture of the big trout before the contest closed on Saturday.

When Wilbur came home from school, Ron was in the workshop. He was fitting a cover to a cage of wooden slats and wire netting that he had made. Later he headed for the falls pool, carrying the cage and his best fishing rod in its plaid cover.

Grimly silent, Ron stood at the head of the pool and cast a lure. All too well he knew what he was doing. Now the freedom that Flash had known all his life was to end.

Almost to an inch Ron knew where Flash would be lurking. As the gaily colored lure touched the water, the rainbow rose to it.

With a swift lift of his forearm, Ron struck. The rod tip bent, and Flash was hooked.

Like a silver arrow he shot downstream. Then he curved upward in a leap that broke the surface in a small explosion. Falling back with a sudden twist, he slapped the water with his widespread tail. On and on he raced.

The reel sang as the line whipped out behind the rushing fish. The slender rod bent with the strain, and Ron fought to keep a firm grip on it.

Again the fighting trout leaped. He swerved, dodged, made one long dazzling rush, and jumped

three times in quick succession. But always the thin, transparent leader on the line kept its steady drag on the trout's head.

Ron gave the fish more line. It whizzed off the reel as Flash charged down the falls pool. Ron was on the defensive during these enraged flurries. But he was sure that the power of those broad fins would soon lessen. Slowly he reeled in some of the line he had lost.

"Flash will be done for in a minute," he thought. "Then I'll be able to guide him into the cage."

But the big rainbow was only beginning to fight. Up the pool he surged in one terrific rush. Ron, knowing that a slack line often means victory for a fish, reeled frantically. Would the big fellow never tire?

Time after time Flash renewed his struggle. A few minutes more of savage give-and-take, and his flanks weakened. With heaving gills he lay on his side at the surface.

Ron kept wishing he had found another way. It was like treachery to conquer this courageous, untamed fighter that he had so long befriended. But he knew that because of the freshet it had to be this or failure. Because of the prize money he dared not fail. Gently he guided the exhausted rainbow into the cage and freed the hook.

After wiring down the cover, Ron sank the cage. It lay securely against the window of the observation pit below the willows.

"He'll be all right," Ron tried to convince himself. "I'll feed Flash well. In a day or two the water will clear. Then I'll let him go and get a good picture."

But all that night in bed Ron lay wide awake, haunted by the thought of the trout having its spirit broken by captivity. Argue with himself as he might, he could not deny that he had selfishly deprived a splendid creature of its freedom.

At daylight Ron stole from the house and hurried to the falls pool. There, vague and ghostly, lay the great trout in his cage, gasping for breath in the silt-laden water. Lifting the sunken cage, the boy yanked off the cover.

With fins and tail frayed from batting the cage, the great rainbow swam off.

That afternoon Ron sent in the best of all his photographic failures. It was the one of Flash putting the invading squawfish to flight. On Saturday night the boy listened to a radio announcer at River City name the winner of the Tourist Bureau's prize. Though several other contestants were given honorable mention, there was no reference to Ron's picture.

The next Monday evening a car drove up, and a gray-haired man got out and came to the house.

"Are you Ron Lincoln?" the stranger asked with a smile. "I'm Professor Howard."

Ron recognized the name, but he was too astonished to speak. Why had this famous naturalist, who was head of the State Conservation Board, come to see him? What could it mean?

"I believe you took this photograph," Professor Howard was saying.

Ron looked at the blurred snap of Flash and the squawfish. He nodded.

"Will you tell me why you took it?" asked Ron's visitor.

Ron spoke hesitatingly at first. But the kindly manner of Mr. Howard soon reassured the boy. As he talked, his listener nodded encouragingly now and then. Thus the youth was led to reveal his dreams for the future.

"But tell me," the man urged, "how did you come to be so interested in underwater wildlife?"

"I don't know, sir," Ron answered. "I was born that way, I guess. Sometimes I sit at that pit window and imagine I can pretty nearly tell what those fish are thinking. You see, I don't know the scientific names or anything——"

"Mere labels," the professor broke in. "Anyone can learn them. Training's needed, of course, but you have something that no amount of training can give. In conservation we always have room for lads like you. Fact is, that's why I came."

And to the astonished boy he offered a summer's job with the State Conservation Board. Ron was to help collect nature specimens—and for pay!

Men of Progress

The River Finds a Master

"Look there, Mr. Ellis!" Mary Shreve cried to the man standing beside her on the dock. "The *George Washington* is moving down into the water."

"Watch it go!" shouted a man behind Mary Shreve. He was one of the many excited spectators crowding the Ohio River wharf at Louisville, Kentucky. It was a summer afternoon in 1824.

"Humph!" sneered a loud voice from the crowd. "It'll capsize! Henry Shreve is crazy to have built a boat that's top-heavy!"

Then came an expectant silence. Everyone was waiting to see if the high, double-decked boat with its special side paddles could stay afloat.

Mary Shreve finally broke the stillness. "It does work!" she shouted. "Just look at it go—like a great white bird skimming over the water!"

Mr. Ellis sighed with relief. "I myself wasn't completely sure that it would work," he admitted to Mrs. Shreve. "Now, madam, I'm convinced that your husband can do a better job of building and running river boats than any man in the United States!"

Henry Shreve had been operating his boats up and down the Ohio and Mississippi rivers for more than ten years. Up until now, however, no riverman had been able to solve the two great problems that hindered river navigation. Occasional stretches of shallow water often caused the deep-hulled boats to go aground. Snags made up of tree roots and masses of river debris caused serious damage to boats that struck them.

The *George Washington* had been designed to overcome both hazards. Shreve's new boat was almost flat-bottomed. Thus it could move through even the most shallow sections of the river. In addition, the craft was easy to steer. It allowed the pilot to avoid any snags he could spot.

After the trial run of the *George Washington*, no one could consider it a failure. There were many eager passengers because it furnished comfortable accommodations. It also was the safest boat on the river.

However, Captain Shreve was not satisfied. He was convinced that all river travel should be safe, and it was not. Each stop he made in a port city brought reports of lives lost when a boat had been sunk by a hidden snag. On every trip the captain saw new wreckage of once sturdy vessels that had come to grief.

At his home one day Henry Shreve sat brooding about the problem. "There must be a way to clear the river," he insisted to his wife.

"You haven't had much trouble with snags," Mary replied. "Why do you worry so much?"

"Just because one of my boats has never been sunk does not mean that one never will be," Henry said. "The snags get worse every day." It was true. The snags were notorious. Shipowners all up and down the rivers were complaining about the vast amount of destruction caused by snags.

Unable to dismiss the problem from his mind, Henry Shreve devised an experimental boat. He was certain that it could remove snags.

Vainly he tried to get the government engineers to build a large, workable model. But instead, the engineers chose to try to remove the snags by a method that another man had suggested. This plan failed, and Henry Shreve tried once more to get the government to construct his snagboat. Then on December 10, 1826, good news arrived by mail. Henry had been appointed the Superintendent of Western River Improvements. Now at long last he might be given a chance to build his boat.

When Mary Shreve heard the news, she shook her head in dismay. "Do you mean that you're going to accept the appointment?" she asked her husband. "Why, you'll be away from home almost all the time. You'll have to let someone else manage your shipyard and run your steamboats. Worst of all, no matter how well you do your job, no one will ever be satisfied with what you accomplish."

"I know," sighed Henry Shreve. "But the river obstructions must be removed. The future of the whole western part of the United States depends on it. River travel is our only good means of transportation. If we are ever to build up the country, we must make our rivers safe for boats. I believe that I can get those snags out. And I shan't be content until I have proved it."

"All right," Mrs. Shreve agreed half-heartedly. "I cannot really blame you. Go ahead and build the boat." With a smile of affection she added, "Good luck, Henry!"

But even as Superintendent of Western River Improvements, Henry Shreve was not immediately permitted to build his boat. The men who had to give the final approval for the project were not sure that his boat could do the job successfully. But in spite of their doubts, Captain Shreve finally won his opportunity. On June 27, 1828, work was begun on his snagboat.

Each day groups of onlookers came to watch the progress of the shipbuilders. Just as there had been resistance to the idea that the *George Washington* would stay afloat, people were now convinced that Henry's snagboat was a waste of money. Day after day the discussion raged.

"Steam power will never root out the snags in the Mississippi and the Ohio," one man declared. "Nothing will ever get rid of them!"

"Oh, I think they can be removed," disagreed another. "But not with a boat of any kind. A boat will be wrecked the first time it comes up against a snag. Those things will have to be taken out of the river with a block and tackle."

Meanwhile, Henry's peculiar craft took shape. It was really two boats. They were built side by side and connected in front by a heavy, wedge-shaped beam of wood. This stout, protruding beam was a huge battering ram, intended to strike a snag and break it up. In designing this unusual vessel, Shreve had planned that the force of the ram's battering blows would be borne by every section of the craft. Thus no single part of it would be jarred loose or broken into splinters.

A year later, in August, 1829, the clumsy-looking vessel was finally launched. Captain Shreve had chosen Plum Point on the Mississippi for his first trial. In that area the worst snag—the terror of every boatman—was to be found.

Men, women, and children stood on the dock and gaped as Shreve's double vessel pulled away. All along the way downstream, people watched the odd craft from the riverbanks. Men on steamboats, rafts, and barges shouted jeering remarks at the strange-looking contraption.

When it finally approached the snag's location, some of the smaller boats began to fall in behind Shreve's vessel. Soon it had a large audience for its snag-breaking test.

In his pilot house Captain Shreve was confident that his boat would not fail its test. Cautiously he maneuvered it close to the huge jumble of partly submerged river debris.

Then he barked the order, "Full steam ahead!" Using every bit of power the engines could muster, he steered his boat head on at the snag!

It was a tremendous collision. Water churned, and the crash of splintering wood filled the air.

For an instant the onlookers feared that the boat had been shattered. But no such thing had happened. The spectators were hearing the sounds of the immense snag being broken to bits. Henry's boat had done its job!

Captain Shreve calmly ordered his crew to pull the chunks of wood out of the river. These he used to stoke the fires in the powerful boilers of his twin vessel. The spectators, who had waited to see Henry Shreve's crazy idea fail, now saluted his great victory with wild cheers.

Until he retired in 1841, Henry continued his work of clearing large rivers. His snagboats successfully removed obstructions from the Ohio, Mississippi, and Missouri rivers. Even the badly jammed Red River was cleared.

Henry did not make the fortune he could have made by continuing his profitable river trade. But he had the satisfaction of performing a great service for the merchant shippers and the pilots who used the waterways that he had opened.

A final honor came to Shreve from the people of Louisiana. They gratefully named one of their cities for the man who had turned snag-obstructed streams into busy thoroughfares. They called the city Shreveport.

Cyrus Does It

"Cyrus, I need an extra man today. You'll have to help cut wheat in that forty near the workshop."

"I'll be glad to, Father," said the farm lad. Taking the cradle, he went off to the field.

From the time the seeds had sprouted, Cyrus had watched that forty acres change. First the green shoots had pushed up through the fertile soil of the Virginia valley near the Blue Ridge Mountains. The shoots had grown until they were more than knee-high. Then gradually they had changed from green to gold—the shimmering gold of ripe wheat.

Now Cyrus was to try his hand at reaping the grain.

From *Children of Necessity*, by Grace Humphrey. Copyright, 1925, 1953. Used by special permission of the publishers, The Bobbs-Merrill Company.

The fifteen-year-old boy eagerly began his task. But an hour later he was gasping for breath, and perspiration was rolling down his face. His back ached with the steady swing, swing, swing of the heavy cradle as swath after swath of wheat was cut. Soon his head began to ache; then he felt himself growing dizzy from the burning heat of the summer sun.

Cutting wheat was not so simple an undertaking as it had looked. Still it must be done despite the torments of heat and exhaustion. The wheat was ripe. It must be cut immediately or the whole crop could be ruined by wind, a heavy rain, or a sudden hailstorm.

All morning the lad worked. During his moments of rest, he thought about the other men who from Bible times until now had done backbreaking work cultivating the land. It was certainly strange that no easier methods had ever been invented.

While he rested in the yellow wheat stubble, he resolved to make a cradle that would be easier to handle. But was that all he could do?

"Come out to the shop and work side by side with me," said his father when Cyrus presented his idea. "Maybe I can help you."

Robert McCormick was a skilled toolmaker and had invented many labor-saving devices. He had made these in the farm blacksmith shop. It was

equipped for real work, with two forges, an anvil,
and a carpenter's bench. Here all kinds of wood
and iron implements were constructed for the house,
the sawmill by the brook, and the flour mills. And
here it was that Cyrus came to whittle out a cradle
light enough to lift easily.

For a while he watched his father hammering a
new piece of iron and shaping it into a rod. "What
are you making now?" Cyrus asked.

Robert McCormick glanced at a queer-looking
apparatus that was set in a corner. "What am I
making?" he asked. "Something to help my reaper
work, perhaps. And if this invention does work,

it won't have any backaches. It won't mind the blazing sun burning down on it. It won't have to stop and rest and take a drink of cider every time it walks around the field.

"Why, my boy," he added with a merry look, "it won't walk around by itself at all. It will be pulled around the field by a horse. There'll be no more backbreaking drudgery, Cyrus, at harvest time, if this works."

But unfortunately it did not work. The test of Robert McCormick's reaper took place some years afterwards, late in the spring of 1831, on a rolling field of green wheat. At first the machine worked well. But on uneven ground the stalks bunched and clogged the knife blades so that the machine ran over the wheat without cutting it at all. Where the ground was perfectly level, the wheat was cut properly. But even then it was tossed all about by the clumsy machine. If the wheat had been ripe, the snarled stalks would have made the grain wholly unfit for threshing.

This unsuccessful trial left Robert McCormick discouraged and hopeless. "All my plans and hard work gone for nothing!" he complained. "No one can ever straighten out that awful mess. The field looks as if witches had been playing with the wheat. Oh, well, forty-six other men have tried to invent a reaper. They all failed miserably, too.

"Take the thing back to the shop, Cyrus. I won't bother working on it any more. Cutting wheat is drudgery—terrible drudgery. And all it has ever given the farmer is a mere living. My old dream of ending this drudgery is over right now. My reaper won't reap! It's not practical. I'm through with it forever!"

But Cyrus did not give up. One day when he and his father were working together, Cyrus glanced at the discarded machine. It lay in disgrace in one corner of the shop. What was the matter with it? Could it possibly be made to work? Could he, Cyrus, fix it so that it would reap successfully?

"Father, do you mind if I take a try at fixing up your reaper?" he asked.

"Do you reckon you can win where I failed, and forty-six other men besides?" Robert McCormick asked his son. "I spent fifteen long years on that reaper, thinking and working, trying this and experimenting with that. I'm afraid it's a hopeless dream. But," he added with a smile, "if you really want to see what you can do, go right ahead, Son."

Cyrus walked over to the reaper and sat down to study the various parts. "Surely there's a way to make this thing cut wheat properly," he thought. "Men can't go on using a cradle forever! Even the strongest farmer cannot cut more than two acres of wheat a day. A day means twelve to sixteen hours of hard work. A reaper would save time and labor. It would save a lot of wheat, too!"

There was always ample time during the spring season to plow the fields and sow the wheat. But the harvest season was usually very short—ten days, sometimes only a week. If the ripe wheat was not cut within those few days, the stalks would begin to break and fall. Then the grain would shell out, and a hard rain would probably ruin the crop.

So Cyrus began to tinker with his father's failure. Just what could he do to make it work when the wheat stood up straight, when it was matted, when it was beaten down by wind or rain? How could he fix the machine so that it would do more than merely cut? He must calculate some way to make it handle each stalk of wheat properly after cutting so that the grains would not shatter.

This job took time and much patience. Yet all the things that Cyrus did to improve the reaper seemed simple to him. He wondered why no man had thought of them before. He found a way to make the machine separate the stalks and hold them upright while being cut. He fashioned a huge wooden reel that gathered the grain in front of the reaper and swept it toward the cutting knife. He added a platform to the machine to catch the stalks as they were cut. This would prevent them from being tossed about on the ground in a tangled mass.

Now the wheat could easily be gathered into sheaves, ready for threshing.

Some of these improvements were Cyrus' own ideas. Some of them had come from his father and other inventors. But no one had ever before put all these ideas together in a single machine.

All the new parts for the machine—cranks, gears, blades of steel, a wooden reel—were hammered or whittled into shape by young Cyrus. He worked desperately to get the reaper finished before the harvest season was over.

"Will you leave one field of wheat uncut until I get my reaper in working order?" Cyrus begged his father.

"Yes, indeed," promised Robert McCormick as he started off to cut wheat the old way, by hand. "I know what it means to have only a few days to try out an idea. I'll give you as much time as I can possibly afford."

Near the end of July, just six weeks after his father's unsuccessful attempt to cut the green wheat, Cyrus' reaper was ready. The lad hitched a farm horse to his unwieldy machine and clattered out of the barnyard. Into the wheat field he went, where the ripe golden grain waited to be cut.

Young McCormick's sisters and brothers looked on, excited and anxious. Mr. and Mrs. McCormick also watched with keen interest and great hopes.

Around and around went the reel, sweeping the stalks of wheat toward the cutting knife. Forward and back and to the side shot the blade. Its sharp metal teeth sheared the dry wheat neatly.

With each click, click, click, bunches of golden grain fell in tidy heaps on the platform. Then a farm hand raked it off into sheaves.

The loose-jointed machine was crudely made. It creaked and groaned as it joggled up and down the field. It was ugly and noisy and clumsy besides. But it worked!

From the look of joy on his mother's face, Cyrus knew how happy she was to see that his reaper was a success.

"I'm proud, Son!" exclaimed Robert McCormick. "Proud to have you win where I failed."

But Cyrus was not completely satisfied. The new machine was practical, but the reel worked poorly. It should be made so that even the lowest stalks of grain would not escape being cut.

After making a few needed improvements, Cyrus gave a public exhibition of his wonderful invention for the farmers of the vicinity. At a nearby farm he cut six full acres of oats in one afternoon. This was a tremendous task for even six men with cradles, an astonished farmer admitted.

The next year, when Cyrus was twenty-three, he took his reaper to a farm near Lexington. There he had an audience of one hundred people who had heard of the new invention. Among them were college professors as well as farmers. There were farm laborers whose hands were calloused by harvest toil that paid five cents an hour for a sixteen-hour day.

Cyrus started the team of horses that pulled his monster machine. Click, click went the teeth of the reaper's sharp steel blade. Again the stalks fell in neat piles onto the platform built to catch the golden grain.

But soon Cyrus reached a very rough section of the field. The reaper jolted this way and that. As it slipped and bounced over the humps, the wheat was hacked off unevenly.

The owner of the farm gestured frantically. "This won't do, mister! Stop your team, I say! Why, you're shattering the grains out of the heads of wheat. You're ruining my crop!"

"This reaper is a humbug," jeered one spectator.

"Give me the old cradle," called another.

The inventor's face turned chalky white at these affronts. His heart hammered wildly. Was he to meet only laughter and ridicule? Was his reaper a flat failure under difficult conditions?

"I'll give you a chance to try reaping on a level field, young fellow," called a friendly voice. "Come, men, lend a hand here! Pull that rail fence down. We can go right in on my land."

This was just what Cyrus wanted—a level field of wheat. Again he called to his horses. Again the reaper began to click. Before sunset Cyrus had succeeded in cutting six acres of grain!

Shouting praises for this amazing performance, the farmers trooped after the clattering machine as it finished the last dozen feet. Across the stubble and out onto the road the cheering men marched. They acted like boys running after a circus parade.

This noisy procession wound its way into the town of Lexington. Hounds yipped, and children yelled as the machine moved forward. Townspeople stared at the strange sight.

"A right smart curious sort of apparatus," said one critical observer of the reaping machine. "But I don't think it will ever come to much."

In the town square, Cyrus McCormick stopped his horses. Crowds moved closer to study this new machine—to see the reel and to touch the keen blade of the cutting knife. Many inquired what the huge, clumsy object was for.

A dignified professor from the Lexington Academy looked it over and heard what it had accomplished that afternoon. "This is an astonishing machine," he announced. "It is worth at least one hundred thousand dollars!"

Cyrus McCormick could scarcely believe the words he had heard. As he rode homeward in the warm twilight, his eyes were filled with awe.

"A hundred thousand dollars!" he whispered half aloud. "No, that's a dream as far away as that twinkling star over the mountains. But whether or not I make much money, I've achieved something worth while. I've invented a better way to harvest grain. Farmers will plant more wheat. People will have more bread. Soon there will be less hunger in the world."

141

It Talks!

Late one Saturday afternoon in 1876, Alexander Graham Bell hastened toward an exhibition hall at the Philadelphia Centennial Exposition. The weather was extremely hot, and the large bag he carried seemed heavier every minute. He was tired and hungry after his train trip from Boston. But he had taken time for only a roll and a cup of tea in the station. Now he was hurrying to get to the exhibition hall before it closed for the day.

Tomorrow the young man would display a device that he had invented while teaching at a school for the deaf. A judging committee, composed of scientists and other important men, would inspect the exhibits. Afterwards an award for the most outstanding new invention would be presented.

At any other time Bell might have lingered to gaze at all the extraordinary buildings. They had been built for this fair, which was in honor of the first hundred years of the United States as an independent nation. But the young Bostonian was too flurried to be interested in buildings now.

Soon he arrived at the exhibition hall, a vast structure covering twenty acres. At the entrance he showed his exhibitor's pass. A guard inspected it carefully. Then he said, "All right," and swung open the admission gate.

Adapted from: *Mr. Bell Invents the Telephone* by Katherine B. Shippen. Reprinted by permission of RANDOM HOUSE, Inc. Copyright, 1952, by Katherine B. Shippen.

Inside the hall the young inventor joined the long stream of visitors who stopped to peer at bicycles, engines, and printing presses. But he did not pause to look at these exhibits of progress. Bell went directly to the corner of the East Gallery where his invention, the telephone, would be displayed.

It did not take long to assemble his instrument. The receiver, transmitter, and batteries were soon hooked together on a table. Next, Bell ran a copper wire from these all the way to the far end of the hall. There he installed a second set of telephone parts. When that was done, he set up a modest sign on his display. Since there seemed to be nothing more to do, he decided to leave and get some rest.

Early the next morning Willie Hubbard, a friend of Bell's, arrived from Boston to help demonstrate the telephone. Together they went out to the exhibition building, which was closed to the public that Sunday morning. Here and there exhibitors were making last-minute adjustments in their displays. But most of the men sat idly chatting while awaiting the judges.

Alexander Bell still could think of nothing more that needed to be done to his exhibit. So he and Willie sat down beside it. Slowly the hours passed. Finally a door opened at the front of the hall. The judges in their stovepipe hats and long frock coats came into view.

At each exhibit the judges paused for a little while. Sometimes an approving nod, sometimes a whisper accompanied their critical study of each display. Deliberately they worked their way down a long aisle, coming closer and closer to the telephone displayed by Alexander Bell.

"Aleck, look," Willie hissed excitedly, pointing to a distinguished-looking man. "That must be Sir William Thomson from England. People say he's the greatest scientist in the world today."

"Yes, and the man next to him is Joseph Henry from the Smithsonian Institution," Aleck declared.

"Who's the heavy-set man with the reddish hair and the square-cut beard?" Willie asked.

Bell stared across the space still separating him and the judges. "Why, I know that man!" he said. "I've talked to him. He came to Boston University and visited the classroom where I was teaching my deaf pupils. He was interested in learning about the school's methods of instruction. We talked for a long time—or at least I did."

"But who is the man?" asked Willie Hubbard. He was exasperated at this long explanation when all he wanted was to be told the man's name.

"He comes from Brazil," Bell continued. "His name is *Dom* Pedro. He's the emperor."

"*Dom* Pedro!" Willie exclaimed. "Why didn't you say so? He's the guest of honor of the whole fair! Did you say you had talked to him?"

"Yes. In Boston."

Now the judges were near enough to Bell's table to be plainly seen.

"My! They look hot," Willie murmured. "Hot and tired!"

Soon the judges reached the exhibit just beside the telephone display. They were so near that it was easy to hear what they were saying.

"Gentlemen," Sir William Thomson said in his clear English voice, "if you will inspect this one display, we shall halt our inspections and continue our judging tomorrow morning. This oppressive American heat makes it impossible to go on."

As the weary men tried to focus their attention on the adjoining exhibit, Bell gasped with dismay. "That's the end of my hopes," he muttered. "Tomorrow I shall be on the train to Boston. I must get back to teach my classes."

Despondently Aleck and Willie watched as the judges turned to leave. Sir William Thomson waited politely for *Dom* Pedro to precede him. But the emperor, who was a man of curiosity, had turned to see what the small exhibit on the next table might be. At that moment he recognized Alexander Graham Bell.

"Why, Mr. Bell!" *Dom* Pedro said, striding up with outstretched hand. "How are things going in Boston? What are these odd-looking objects that you are showing here?"

At once Bell began explaining the telephone. "Unfortunately," he concluded, "I am obliged to return to Boston tonight. I'm sorry that you and the other judges are leaving before you see how my invention works."

"But that is impossible!" *Dom* Pedro said. "Of course we must see it now." Turning back to the departing committee, he spoke with insistence. "I must ask you to wait, gentlemen. This is Mr. Bell of Boston. He has made what he calls a telephone. He cannot stay until tomorrow to show it to us. We must see it now."

Wearily the judges returned. They could not ignore the request of the guest of honor.

"The telephone is a device by which the human voice may be carried along an electric wire," *Dom* Pedro explained, carefully repeating Bell's words. "A person standing at the other end of the wire can hear the speaker distinctly—just as though he were standing right by the speaker's side."

There was no comment from the judges. One of them looked bored, and one doubtful. The others merely looked hot.

"Will Mr. Bell demonstrate?" Sir William asked.

Aleck Bell walked to the far end of the exhibition hall and picked up the telephone instrument. He waited for the hum and click which meant that Willie Hubbard had turned on the battery current. Bell spoke into the transmitter. "All right."

"It's ready," Willie told the assembled gentlemen. "Your Majesty, will you listen first?"

Dom Pedro stepped forward and accepted the metal box that Willie handed him.

"Hold it close to your ear, Sir," Willie advised.

Dom Pedro nodded. There was a moment's pause as the emperor listened and the others watched.

All of a sudden an expression of surprise mingled with disbelief appeared on *Dom* Pedro's face. "It talks!" he exclaimed. "It talks!"

Sir William took the instrument. He spoke into the box. The box answered him at once. "This is extraordinary," the scientist murmured.

A third judge stepped forward and placed the box to his ear. "I hear a voice speaking quite plainly," he announced.

The excited judges forgot the heat and dismissed all thoughts of leaving. Again they passed the receiver from one to another.

"This invention will change the way people live all over the world," *Dom* Pedro predicted. "Without doubt it should receive the Centennial award."

And it did!

Wizard of the Air

"Guglielmo," *Signora* Marconi admonished her son, "you study too much. This summer you must go to the mountains with your brother Luigi and forget those books and magazines on science."

Dutifully the twenty-year-old Guglielmo went off to spend the summer of 1894 in the mountains of northern Italy with his brother. But he took along the books and journals that he loved.

One day he saw an article that stirred him to great excitement.

Eagerly he read of a man named Hertz and his amazing discovery. Hertz had found that the sparks made with a machine called an exciter produced electric waves. These waves passed through the air without the need of wires and made sparks appear on another machine called a coherer.

Guglielmo's eyes opened wide at the startling idea. Carefully he reread the long article. If it was true, why had Hertz simply made the discovery and stopped? Marconi took a deep breath. Why had Hertz experimented no further? If sparks could be transmitted from an exciter to a coherer through the air without a connecting wire, surely messages could be transmitted in the same manner.

Young Marconi spent the rest of the summer reading everything he could find on electricity and electric waves. For hours he sat and considered what might be done with the Hertz discovery.

Eventually the vacation period was over. Back at his home he begged his mother for the use of the two big rooms in the attic of the house.

"I must have the space for my very own use," he insisted. "No one must come in or disturb me."

"Not even to clean?" exclaimed his mother.

"Not even to clean!" replied the young man.

With a sigh the *signora* gave her son permission to use the attic. Day after day she watched him disappear into his workshop. She worried because her son ate irregularly and slept very little. Yet she did not interfere.

In his workroom Marconi built an exciter and a coherer thirty feet apart. He wired his coherer to a bell that would ring if an electric spark on the exciter should create a spark on the coherer. After a full month of work he finally pressed the switch that created a spark. It leaped on the exciter and crackled in the air. Yet at the coherer, thirty feet away, there was only dead silence. The bell had not sounded.

Marconi touched the switch again. Still there was silence. Undaunted, the young scientist started all over again to build a new coherer. In another month he was ready to try again. Quickly he made a final adjustment. Then his sensitive finger once more pressed the switch on the exciter. A bluish spark jumped. This time the bell on the coherer rang out clearly. A few days later he was able to ring a bell on the lawn from a spark created in the attic.

At one of these experiments Guglielmo's father was a spectator. "Yes, yes," the hard-headed banker said to his son. "You can ring the bell. But what practical use does this nonsense have? Bells can be made to ring by simpler means."

"Yes, they can," Marconi agreed readily. "But with a similar and more powerful apparatus I could send messages for many miles."

Signor Marconi thought for a few minutes. "I do not say it cannot be done," he said doubtfully. "You have proved to me that your electric waves travel from the attic out to the lawn, two hundred feet away. But will they go farther?"

The young man sighed. It was hard to find the words that would convince another of what he himself was so sure. But slowly he began. "If I were to tell you that the time will come when my waves will travel across the ocean, you might not believe me. Perhaps no one would. Still it will happen. The pioneering steps in wireless communication have already been taken. Last week it was thirty feet; this week two hundred feet; perhaps next week a thousand. Then who knows?"

The elder Marconi rose to his feet. He had to admit that the idea was convincing. "Whatever equipment you need I shall be glad to buy for you," he promised his son.

With his father's approval Guglielmo set out to produce electric waves that would travel greater distances. To achieve this, he invented two devices now called an aerial and a ground. With these he created a stronger spark and also strengthened its reception. He next substituted a telegraph key for the switch on the exciter. Then he fixed the coherer so that it would click out dots and dashes like a Morse telegraph receiver.

Soon it was time to make another test. The lad had moved his coherer to the dome of a hill almost a mile from the house. He asked his brother Alfonso to stand beside the coherer and hold a white flag. If the coherer clicked, Alfonso was to wave the flag.

From the window of the attic the inventor kept his eyes on his brother. Tensely he pressed the key and sent the Morse signal for the letter *S*. Then almost simultaneously Alfonso began to bounce up and down, waving the flag.

In later experiments Marconi proved that his wireless code messages hurdled hills and mountains as well as level ground. Then his shrewd father recommended the next step in his son's career. He no longer needed proof that the work had value. He believed in it. Now his son must persuade others to give him additional support.

Many people to whom Guglielmo talked and wrote about the wireless could not imagine how such an invention might be useful. But in England a few men saw a real need for communication with their ships at sea. So Marconi was invited to England to show his wireless equipment. The demonstration proved so impressive that several Englishmen formed a manufacturing company with Marconi. The company would make wireless sets.

By 1900, messages were being sent for distances of more than one hundred fifty miles. The British Navy had installed wireless equipment on twenty-six of its ships. The Navy had also instructed the company to build six land stations.

But Marconi was not completely satisfied with the progress that wireless communication was making. At a meeting of the company directors one day the young man rose to his feet.

"Gentlemen," he said, "the time has come to act."

"Act?" one of the directors replied, smiling. "I think we're acting rather effectively now."

"Acting effectively, perhaps, but not progressing," Marconi answered. "Two hundred fifty watts of battery-supplied power is no longer enough. What we need now is a permanent power station capable of producing twenty-five thousand watts."

No one at the meeting spoke for a long moment. Finally a voice whispered, "But—but why?"

"I want to build a powerful station in England," Marconi began slowly, "and another in America. Then a ship leaving England will be able to remain in communication with England for the first half of its trip. As it moves out of the range of the English station, it will come into the range of the American station. Thus a boat can remain in contact with land for its entire voyage."

The directors were startled by the bold idea. But Marconi's calm, assured manner won them over. In July, 1900, work was begun on the first of the high-powered stations. It was located on the southern coast of England. Work on the American station was begun in 1901.

The first test was made from the English station. A receiving set located in an Irish town two hundred twenty-five miles away was tuned to pick up the signal. The waves coming from the English station were so powerful that the coherer rattled. Again and again Marconi tested the waves, always with the same miraculous results.

"Kemp, these waves will go across the Atlantic!" he shouted to one of his assistants.

"Across the Atlantic!" For a moment Kemp could not fathom his meaning. "I thought they were only supposed to reach a ship halfway across."

"Yes, I know. Yet if the waves will cross the ocean, they will reach a ship at any point between here and America."

"Why, of course!" Kemp's eyes had brightened with excitement.

"We will have to cross the ocean to prove this," Marconi continued. "But first we must make more tests here. We must be sure we are right."

In December of 1901 Marconi, Kemp, and another assistant arrived in Newfoundland, Canada. This is the point of land in North America that is closest to England. Here the twenty-seven-year-old inventor would attempt transatlantic wireless communication for the first time.

In an isolated military barracks, heated only by an ancient stove, Marconi unpacked his numerous bulky boxes. Shivering in a drafty room, the three men prepared for their work. They had to install the coils, batteries, coherer, and other necessary materials that had been transported across the ocean. With this equipment they hoped to receive an electric wave that would flash across the vast Atlantic in about one-hundredth of a second.

On Monday, three days after the group arrived, preliminary work was begun. Ground connections were driven into the stubborn frozen earth. Each man took a turn at the job, working as rapidly as possible. But the workers' fingers stiffened in the intense cold, and their clothes hardened from the rain that rapidly turned to ice.

On Tuesday the work of erecting the necessary apparatus continued. The next day, Wednesday, was the day on which the English station had agreed to start transmitting daily signals, between twelve noon and three o'clock. But before Marconi could attempt reception of the signals, his aerial was ripped loose from its moorings by a fierce gale.

Early on Thursday everything was ready. As noon approached, the men grew tense. At last Marconi walked across the room. With deliberate movements he lifted the telephone receiver that he had connected to the coherer and put it to his ear.

His two assistants watched his intent expression. They could not tell whether or not the signal was coming through. Marconi's face gave no clue.

Then Marconi turned to Kemp, holding out the receiver. "Can you hear anything?"

Kemp flattened a hand against one ear to shut out the howling of the Newfoundland wind. He cradled the receiver against the other ear. After a moment he said, "Indeed I can. Distinctly!"

"Yes," said Marconi. "I heard it, too." Now he allowed himself to smile.

But he waited one more day to hear the signal again before giving his big news to the papers. On December 15, 1901, the *New York Times* headlines gave the information he finally released.

WIRELESS SIGNALS ACROSS THE ATLANTIC
MARCONI SAYS HE HAS RECEIVED THEM FROM ENGLAND

Proof of the accomplishment was not yet available to anyone except Marconi and his aids. So the news story that followed was very short. But the sending of wireless code messages across the ocean was soon to become a common occurrence. And Guglielmo Marconi lived to see the day when the miracle of sending voices and music through the air was just as commonplace.

Machine Crazy

"Pa, stop!" young Henry Ford shouted, standing up in the farm wagon. "There's something I want to see—an engine without horses to pull it."

Henry and his father were face to face with an immense iron vehicle moving along by its own power. It was a steam engine and boiler mounted on huge wheels, with a water tank and coal cart trailing behind. As the clumsy monster bumped and rumbled down the road, sooty clouds of smoke and cinders billowed from the tall stack.

Henry jumped out of the wagon and darted across the road to the noisy machine.

"Say, mister," he cried to the driver, "may I look at your engine?"

The man pulled a lever and stopped the vehicle.

"What makes it move? How does it work? What can it do? Where are you going with it?" Henry asked, all in one breath.

"Hold on, young fellow!" the driver said. "One question at a time."

"Where are you going with it?" Henry repeated as he walked around the engine, absorbing each detail.

"I'm driving it to Dearborn to run threshing machines, sawmills, and the like," replied the man. Then he showed the lad how he shoveled coal into the boiler and how the engine was steered when it lumbered down the road under its own steam.

"Come on, Henry," Mr. Ford called. "Let's go!"

"Just a minute, Pa," Henry begged. "The man hasn't shown me how the steam is generated."

But Henry did not get a chance to find out. His father had already started the horses, and Henry had to run to catch up with the wagon.

During the next four years Henry grew increasingly dissatisfied with farm work. He felt that he must go to nearby Detroit, where he could learn all about engines. At last he attempted to explain his feelings to his father. "Pa, I don't know how to tell you," Henry said. "But it's just about the hungriest kind of feeling a fellow ever had."

"Now, Son," Mr. Ford admonished. "This engine talk is a silly fad. Sensible people will soon forget it."

161

"Times are changing," Henry argued. "More and more things are being done with machines and being done better."

"Don't you believe it," Mr. Ford insisted. "How could a machine make a better set of harness than old Si Henricks has been making for forty years? And take Jed Martin, the cobbler. No machine can make as fine a pair of shoes as he can. Besides, all machines break down. They're not dependable."

Henry shook his head and laughed. "People will learn to repair machines and build better ones."

"Well," said Mr. Ford, "go to the city if you wish. Get all this strange machine craziness out of your head. Then come back to the farm."

The nine-mile walk to Detroit was only a jaunt to the lad. He soon found a job in a machine shop and made swift progress in learning mechanics. In 1881, after two years of training, he was sent out to repair engines and teach people to operate them.

The more Henry saw of machines, the less he wanted to return to Dearborn. But when a letter came saying that his father was ill and needed him, Henry knew that he must return home. There was one good thing about it. He would have more time to experiment with new kinds of engines. So back to the farm he went.

When Henry's neighbors saw him working in the fields, they no doubt decided that he had had enough of engines and the city. This idea never occurred to Henry. He had no thought of settling down on the farm permanently.

The first thing he did was to fix up his workshop. The lathe, vise, forge, and anvil that had once served him well were now replaced by new equipment. He had a better forge, a lathe driven by foot power, a drilling machine, and excellent hand tools. Now the farm shop had a skilled machinist in command, instead of just a clever boy who enjoyed working with tools.

When young Henry Ford married, his father gave him some land of his own. Henry ran his farm even better than he had managed his father's. His methodical training as a mechanic was a big help. It enabled him to organize the work and get it done without overworking the hired hands.

In the evenings while his wife, Clara, cleared away the supper dishes, Henry would get out his engineering books and magazines. These he read from cover to cover.

One spring night Henry startled his wife by saying, "Clara, they're on the right track!"

"What track?" Clara asked patiently.

"A horseless carriage! Some Frenchman has invented a horseless carriage. Do you suppose I could build one, too?"

Clara looked at her husband, who seemed so very serious. "I'm sure you could," she replied. "But why bother? We have everything we need."

"It wouldn't be just for us," explained Henry. "It would make a new kind of life for people."

"Well, Henry," said his wife, "if you want to do it, you will. When you once make up your mind to do something, there's no turning you aside."

All summer Henry planted and plowed and tended the cattle. But his mind was concentrated on how to build a gasoline engine. In the fall the Fords left the farm and moved to Detroit.

How the city had grown! It was twice as large as it had been ten years before, when Henry had first walked to town to learn about steam engines. There were many new factories. More electricity was being used, and the Edison Electric Company needed men to operate their generators. Henry's accurate knowledge of steam engines helped him secure a job at one of the company's substations.

The substation current was generated by steam engines. Henry's job was to keep them in working order. This gave him an opportunity to consider ways of solving a big problem in building gasoline engines. For he had decided that electricity would somehow have to supply a steady spark to explode the fuel for power.

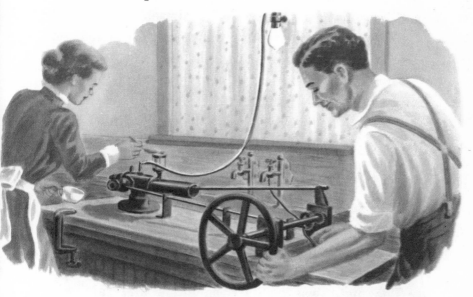

For one experiment Henry had mounted his engine on a wooden board clamped to the kitchen sink. His wife stood by his side, patiently dropping gasoline from a teaspoon into a little cup attached to the cylinder. When the engine finally produced steady explosions, a smile of great satisfaction covered Henry Ford's face.

Soon after that, Henry sketched his first plans for a motor carriage that would use the engine he had developed. He worked methodically, completing each detail of one part before going on to another. Other men in America and abroad were also trying to build horseless carriages. But Henry had no way of finding out how they were doing it. He had to solve each problem for himself.

Within four years after his task was started, he finished a two-cylinder car. It could not run in reverse; but it did have two speeds—a high of twenty miles an hour and a low of ten.

"It's ready—ready to test!" Henry told Clara. He was so excited that his voice was only a husky whisper.

"But it's late, and it's raining," Clara protested. "Can't you wait till daylight to see if the carriage will run?"

"No. I would jump out of my skin if I had to wait that long!" Henry replied.

The night was as dark as pitch, and rain was pouring down. Henry opened the back door of his workshop and hung a lantern on the vehicle to light the way. Working at the front end of the car, he brought the motor to life. Then he climbed to the seat, seized the steering rod, moved a clutch lever, and started off. The car bumped slowly along the alley and into the street.

Lights appeared in the windows of nearby houses. A few curious souls were peering out to see what was making such a commotion.

At the end of the block Henry turned the vehicle and steered it home. He was master at last of a horseless carriage that was moved by its own power.

"It runs!" he shouted triumphantly to his wife. "Now I must improve it."

During additional trials of Ford's car, word went about that a queer man was driving a very queer contraption on the streets of Detroit. It was considered a nuisance. It made a racket and scared horses. But its worst offense was blocking traffic. A crowd always gathered to look at it. If Henry left it for any length of time, some curious person would try to run it. Finally it had to be chained to a lamppost whenever Henry left it for a while.

While Ford was improving his motorcar, other automobiles were being manufactured. But these were all large and very expensive. Henry felt that a small, cheap car was what most people needed.

When he was thirty-three years old, he met Thomas Alva Edison at a convention of electric companies in New York.

Hearing that Mr. Ford was building a motorcar, Edison was immediately interested. He had Henry explain how his car worked. After the explanation the electrical genius asked all kinds of questions about the gas engine.

"Young fellow, that's the thing," Mr. Edison said at last, bringing his fist down on the banquet table with a bang. "Keep at it!"

With this encouragement Henry Ford began working harder than ever on his second car. When it was finished, it was two feet longer than the first model and could go backward as well as forward.

But Henry's work was just beginning. Building a successful car was only half his dream. The other half was to manufacture his cars cheaply enough for farmers and factory workers to buy them.

In 1903, with the help of some other men, Ford started his factory. The first year he built about seventeen hundred cars. They sold for $850, while other makes sold for as much as $8,000. Henry had been successful in his aim to build a cheap car.

Orders for Ford cars increased, and soon a bigger factory was built to produce more of them. As he manufactured more and more automobiles, Henry learned to make them more efficiently. Thus they became even less expensive.

Before long almost everyone could afford to buy a car. Just as Ford had predicted, the life of the people changed. All over the country men and women discovered that motoring was fun. The machine-crazy lad from Dearborn had put America on wheels.

Nickels and Dimes

Mr. Moore, owner of a big store in Watertown, New York, was an awe-inspiring figure to the shabby young man standing before him on a March morning in 1873. Sitting at his desk on a platform in the rear of the store, the merchant glanced once more at a letter the young man had handed him.

The letter was from Mr. McNeil, a grocer in the village of Great Bend. He had written that the lad had studied bookkeeping and had worked evenings in McNeil's store to get some experience as a clerk. Mr. McNeil had also stated that in his estimation Moore's firm would miss the chance of a lifetime if it did not hire Frank Woolworth.

The merchant scowled as he read. Then he began firing questions thick and fast. Did Frank know how to make out a sales check properly? How to take an inventory? How to measure yard goods? Could he tell all-silk goods from silk-and-cotton?

The young man was overwhelmed by Mr. Moore's questions, and Mr. Moore was shocked at the lad's answers. This greenhorn did not know one single thing that a dry-goods clerk must know!

"I'll learn," Frank promised earnestly. "I can learn very fast. And I don't care how long or how hard I work."

The man studied the sincere face before him. "Is this just an excuse to stay in town for a while? Or do you want to make clerking a steady job?"

"It's the only kind of work I ever want to do, Mr. Moore," young Woolworth said seriously. "I hope it's going to be my whole life's work."

Mr. Moore hesitated a second. Then he said, "All right. We'll give you a chance. But you will have to start at the very bottom. We'll expect you to open packing cases, wash windows, split kindling, keep the stoves going, and carry out the ashes. You'll do the sweeping and cleaning, too, of course. Do you still want the position?"

"Yes, sir, I want to do any kind of work around a store," Frank answered quickly. "Those jobs will suit me fine. When do I start, Mr. Moore? And how much will you pay me?"

"Pay you? Should we pay you for teaching you the business? Why, you young fool, you ought to

171

pay us! But we'll be generous. We won't charge you a cent. If we find out that you're worth anything, we'll start paying you wages in six months. That's my offer. Take it or leave it."

Frank managed to hide his dismay. "Will it be all right if I think it over, sir?" he asked. "I can let you know this afternoon."

"Suit yourself," Mr. Moore said indifferently and turned back to his desk.

Frank Woolworth decided to take the job. But he agreed to go without pay for only three months. After that his wages would be three dollars and fifty cents a week, the cost of his room and board. He would get more later, if his work was satisfactory.

The new clerk soon proved that he was a hard worker, dependable and honest; but he was not a good salesman. He could not bring himself to press a customer to buy. It seemed to him that a buyer had a right to make up his mind. Mr. Moore, and many other merchants, believed otherwise. They thought that a clerk was disgraced when a customer walked out of his store without a purchase.

One night after the store closed, Frank was told to remove the merchandise displayed in the south window and wash the glass. "Then," Mr. Moore added carelessly, "you may retrim the window."

All alone Frank went to work. He had the store's whole stock at his disposal. After cleaning the glass,

he unrolled several lengths of dress material and draped the cloth in graceful folds. Because he liked red, he chose bolts of various shades of red silk. To the folds of bright silk he pinned lacy, white handkerchiefs. Against this colorful background he set pairs of ladies' high-buttoned shoes.

At last he locked the store and started home. The town clock was striking two, but he paused for a final look. Even with no light but the dim street lamp, the window looked perfect to Frank. "It's like a beautiful picture," he thought.

Mr. Moore, coming late to work the next day, observed a knot of women standing before the south window. He slowed his steps and listened to their delighted comments. There was no such audience for the north window, with its uninteresting stacks of blankets and table linen. Nor was anyone looking at the two windows around the corner, where men's wear was somberly displayed.

The store owner proceeded to his office and sent for Woolworth. It was not in Mr. Moore's nature to pay compliments. Without praise he ordered the young man to clean and retrim the other windows as soon as the store closed. "That's part of your job from now on," he added gruffly.

In the summer of 1878 even attractive windows did not bring in business. Store sales were falling off all over the country. Merchants in some cities were trying a new scheme to attract customers. This was a bargain table of five-cent merchandise. There was not much profit in it, but it did bring people into the stores. Then the clerks could try to sell their higher-priced goods. In desperation Mr. Moore decided to try the new idea.

He ordered a trial shipment of five-cent articles. When the stock arrived, he turned it over to young Woolworth. Frank was quick to see the advantage of five-cent goods. Many customers spending a little would be as good as a few customers spending a great deal.

The bargain display was set up for the week of the county fair. Bright-red cloth covered two tables.

On this cloth Frank arranged the five-cent articles. Last of all he lettered and set up a sign. It proclaimed, "Any Article—Five Cents."

The five-cent counter was the sensation of Fair Week. Mr. Moore was not pleased, however. "I don't like it, Frank," he complained. "Cheap goods do not belong in a store like mine. I like to sell only quality merchandise."

"You may be right, sir," Frank agreed. "But I think that a store selling nothing except five-cent goods would be successful. If I had the money for my own store, that's the kind I'd start."

"A five-cent store?" The merchant squinted his shrewd eyes. "It's an idea," he grunted. After a moment he said, "All right, young man. You find a store and set it up. I'll stake you to three hundred dollars' worth of merchandise."

Frank chose Utica, New York, as the location for his store. But though it was a success at first, its sales soon dwindled. Finally Woolworth closed it.

"Why?" the young man asked himself. "The idea is a good one, but something went wrong." At last he thought he knew why the venture had failed. His stock looked cheap and offered little variety. How could it be any better at such a low price?

Immediately Woolworth decided that he would have to abandon the five-cent limit. A five-and-ten-cent store was the answer.

Having made this decision, he opened a second store in Lancaster, Pennsylvania. It was a huge success. As time went on, Woolworth learned to buy the best low-priced goods available. These included notions, household articles, and toys. In a few years, branch stores were opened all over the United States, in England, and in Germany.

When the nickel-and-dime man was sixty years old, his most cherished dream was realized. He erected in New York City the tallest and one of the most beautiful buildings in the world. The Woolworth Building was opened to the public by President Woodrow Wilson. In Washington, on the evening of April 24, 1913, he pressed a button to illuminate the astounding new building.

Great crowds gathered outside to look and marvel at the towering structure ablaze with lights.

Inside, before the invited guests, Frank Woolworth declared that the new sixty-story skyscraper was not a monument to himself. "It's a monument to an idea," he said. "The idea that any customer is entitled to good goods at prices he can afford to pay."

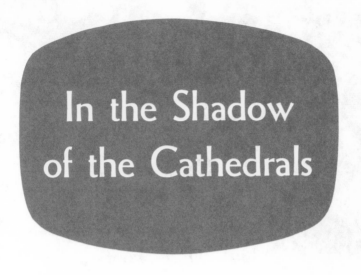

In the Shadow
of the Cathedrals

Little Dusty Foot

Out of the crowd of horsemen rode a magnificent merchant prince. He was everything that Rauf, the little charcoal burner, had dreamed a great *Messire* Dusty Foot would be. The merchant stopped in front of Rauf and the priest, who waited for him beside the broad highway of the Emperor Charlemagne.

"*Messire* Priest, what can I do for you?" asked the merchant. "Why, it's Father Boniface!"

"Yes, Bertin, my son. I'm glad we found you. This boy wants to be a dusty foot and travel the roads like you. He has always wanted to learn your trade. Little Dusty Foot, we call him. Can you take him under your banner?"

178

"I will, Father Boniface," said the merchant.

"*Messire* Bertin will teach you to be a real dusty foot, Rauf," Father Boniface said gently. As Rauf watched his friend depart, he wished only to be back with his father at the charcoal pit in the hills. But there was no help for it. The saints had heard his perhaps foolish prayer, and he would have to be the best traveler he could.

Rauf's pet magpie, Grump, fluttered nervously on his shoulder. The thought that his pet was still with him comforted the boy. He smoothed Grump's feathers.

"Here is your new master, Little Dusty Foot," *Messire* Bertin was saying. Rauf turned to face a stout youth who was mounted on a mule, and was carrying a fife and a drum.

"I'm not really your master. I'm just your master's servant," said the youth. "I'm François. I drum up the crowd before *Messire* Hakim, the great leech, performs feats of magic and sells his cures. Master Hakim has asked *Messire* Bertin for another boy to help roll his pills. Come, hop up with me on my mule. We're going to the next town where we stay for market day."

Soon Rauf saw before him the walls and turrets of a town. The whole company stopped before the bridge gate while *Messire* Bertin, leader of the caravan, rode forward to pay the toll.

Rauf's eyes
widened when he found
himself inside the walls. So
many houses elbowed one another
that he wondered how the good saints could ever
keep track of folk wedged together so tightly. Mud
was deep in the narrow street, and it spattered over
François and Rauf when a pig waddled between the
mule's feet and made her stumble.

At the *Cat and Fiddle Inn* Rauf met his new master, a strange-looking man with a sharp nose and
bushy eyebrows. The two boys ate cabbage soup
and roast wild boar in the inn kitchen. Then François
brought blankets from the saddlebag, and he and
Rauf curled up on the floor near the hearth. Grump,
the magpie, perched on an iron hook overhead.
Soon the inn grew quiet.

Once Rauf awoke when the town watchman banged his iron-tipped staff on the cobblestones outside and boomed, "Pray for the dead. Pray for the dead."

All next day Rauf rolled pills. He pulled the soft insides out of new bread, and put the gummy mess on a big board. The crusts he hid for Grump. Master Hakim separated the sticky bread into four wooden bowls. In one bowl he sprinkled red powder, in a second orange powder, in a third black, in the fourth nothing.

"This is the magic touch, my boy," he confided. "Only the great Hakim knows the secret. Now mix the soft bread and powder. Then roll it into pills. François will show you. I must go and commune with the healing saints." He hurried off.

"The healing saints," François muttered. "It's not the likes of him that saints help. The magic powder? Red clay ground up, saffron, and lamp black. Magic indeed!"

Pills, pills, pills! They were worse than charcoal, Rauf decided. Much good it does one to get into a dusty-foot caravan if all one does is to roll bread dough into pills all day long.

Things change, things change, things change, rang the cathedral chimes. Grump perched on Rauf's shoulder and cried, "Upward and onward. Saint Martin preserve us." Rauf's spirits rose in spite of himself.

Next day the merchants moved on. Through muddy roads they journeyed until in October the caravan drew up to the entrance of the great Fair grounds of Saint Denis near Paris. At the gate each man had to swear that he would not steal, cheat, or weigh wrongly while he was in the Fair grounds.

Messire Bertin paid the entrance fee for each trader, each pack horse, each servant. There was no bargaining over the amount, either, for the Emperor Charlemagne had set down a just price, and no man dared charge more.

Rauf stopped and watched a man with a dancing bear until Master Hakim yelled:

"You, there, Little Dusty Foot! What do you think you are, a customer at this Fair? Unpack my black gown—hang it up—brush it. Look for fleas in the fur. Brush my beaver hat. Polish my sword. Run to the baker yonder and ask when he will have fresh bread. Get your magpie busy on the new words I want him to learn."

Rauf began to do as he was told—shake the black gown, hunt for fleas, brush the hat—only to be called a lazy boy and told to work faster. Grump was fluttering around enjoying the excitement. Every now and then he would fly to some high tree and call, "Hear ye! Hear ye!" Sometimes he would mew like a cat and set the dogs barking.

Now the sellers of cooked sausages and dried fish, the pastry makers, and the fruit and honey sellers were opening their stalls. More merchants had arrived, and the grounds were filling up.

That night Rauf and François and even Master Hakim rolled pills. Boxes and boxes of red, black, orange, and white pills awaited tomorrow's buyers. The leech also made a few special gold pills to cure the knights and rich landholders.

The next morning François spread out a midnight-blue carpet on the stage which the leech had set up. Then he hung curtains adorned with black cats jumping over golden crescents.

Master Hakim yelled at François, who ran to him and brought back a bright red suit with a long tail attached to it, and a cap with two horns.

"Here, Rauf, Master Hakim says you are to join the show. Get into this suit, and when I give the signal, you are to walk across the stage with

183

Grump on your shoulder and have him say, "Buy red pills for your stummick!"

Rauf took one look and crossed himself. "Why, that's an evil spirit's dress! I can't wear it."

"Yes, you can. This is only a play. Doesn't the priest himself play the wicked Herod in the Christmas play?"

"Yes, but Herod wasn't an evil spirit. He was a man."

Perhaps Rauf would have argued longer, but Master Hakim called gruffly, "Hurry, the crowd is already milling through the gates."

Rauf had other misgivings about wearing the red suit once he was in it, because Grump flew around and around before alighting on the unfamiliar red shoulder. "Saint Martin preserve us," croaked the magpie.

François dressed himself in his scarlet tunic and strutted up and down the Fair streets with his fife and drum. He shouted:

"Come to see the great leech Hakim, the mightiest doctor of them all. No matter what troubles you, he has pills to cure. Come! Come! Come!"

Soon François had brought a laughing and wondering crowd to the stage.

"Now do what I said," he ordered Rauf. "Make Grump say what I told you." He threw some powder into a pot of burning charcoal.

Rauf mounted the stage.

The folk roared as the little horned, red-clad figure with the long red tail, and the jet-black magpie perched on his shoulder emerged from the whirling smoke.

François called out, "See the spirit of Hakim."

"Buy red pills for your stummick, Grump," Rauf whispered. "Nice Grump!"

With a mighty flap of black wings, Grump screamed out, "Buy red pills for your stummick. Buy pills. Buy black pills for your liver!"

Howls and yells of delight surged up from the crowd as Rauf disappeared behind a curtain. Master Hakim stalked majestically out to give his pill-selling talk. People hurried to the platform to buy the pills. Business was wonderful.

But before the Fair at Saint Denis was over Master Hakim was in trouble with the law, and had been banished from the Fair grounds forever.

Messire Bertin spoke to Rauf.

"I will give you a choice, Little Dusty Foot," he said. "After the Fair I go to the Northland, to seek amber, falcons, high fur caps, mink, and fish glue from the Russians. You may go with me or you may go with the spice merchant. He has asked for you. He is a good man and will be a better master than Hakim. He goes to the South, to the land of the Moors in Spain."

"Oh *Messire* Bertin, I like you, but I have always longed to go to the Southland," cried Rauf.

Messire Bertin laughed. "You are a born dusty foot, Rauf. I, too, once dreamed of the South—of crystal fountains in groves of orange and myrtle."

He went with Rauf to the stand of the spice merchant and arranged for Rauf's wages. The man smiled kindly and said, "All that remains to be done now, Little Dusty Foot, is to see that you find yourself something to trade with. When we spice merchants take someone like you to learn our business, we always advance his wages and let him pick out something to take with him to sell at a profit in the new market."

Rauf's eyes opened wide. Now he would know what it was to be a real dusty foot.

A Knight in Danger

"Sir Brian brings tidings," cried Patrick, heir to the O'Neills. "King Richard has taken the Cross! He has vowed to go and free the Holy Sepulcher and the Holy Land itself from the Saracens."

"What is that to you, my brother?" The blind boy Alain, twin brother to Patrick, spoke softly, trying to still his sudden fear. Surely Patrick would not want to leave his Irish homeland!

"Sir Brian says I am of full age to gain my spurs," said Patrick. "Where could more honor be won by an untried knight than following the king into battle for the sake of Our Lord's tomb?"

"Our Lord's tomb is but an empty grave," murmured Alain, "for He is risen." The lad frowned. "What of our stepbrother Baldwin? Is he of a mind to get his spurs and go crusading with you?"

"He is ready for knighthood, yes, but he has no wish to go crusading. Our Norman brother covets the lands of the O'Neills. I fear to leave my people in his charge, yet where else can I turn?"

"What of the Lord Abbot?" asked Alain. "He is Irish and he was our father's friend. Can you not leave him in charge?"

"It will anger our stepmother," said Patrick, thinking of the woman of Norman blood their father had married shortly before his death. "But so be it.

"Listen. Tomorrow at the Mass of Daybreak I will take the Crusader's Cross. Then shall announcement be made of my approaching knighthood—mine and Baldwin's. We shall keep our vigil in the chapel that same evening, for there is no time to be lost. There will be no tournament afterward, but Baldwin and I will match our skill with the lance and then we will have a boar hunt for our guests. I will give the castle keys to the Lord Abbot and the people shall swear allegiance to him in the same hour."

"Our Norman kin will indeed be angry, Patrick."

"Even so." Patrick laughed scornfully. "These Norman conquerors grow too proud!"

"Patrick, why do you wish to go to the Holy Land? Is it to free an empty grave from the Saracens? Is it to attain glory for your knighthood?"

Patrick answered softly, "Neither is the true reason, Alain. I believe that the Holy Grail is there. I believe if we could but find the Cup, the gentle Lord would hear my prayer, and you would be given the gift of sight. For you, Alain, shall go with me to the Holy Land!"

When, next evening, a blast of trumpets announced the hour of dinner, folk came running from every quarter of the castle. Another blast of the trumpets announced the arrival at the great hall of the O'Neill and his guests. Patrick was wearing the Crusader's white cloak with its scarlet cross which he had received when he took his vow in the chapel that morning.

After a third blast of trumpets, the Lord Abbot spoke the blessing and the feasting began. Smoking haunches of venison were set on the board beside great pots of rabbit stew, and roasts of pork and quartered sheep. Bread was hacked into thick slices to serve as plate and napkin, and bones were tossed to eager hounds. When the feasting was done, huge baskets were filled with food and taken to the beggars at the castle gates.

At last, preceded by their squires, the young candidates for knighthood each took a lighted beeswax candle and followed the abbot into the chapel. There they knelt before the high altar, on which lay two suits of shining chain mail, two steel helmets, and two shields.

Putting his hands on the shoulders of the two candidates, the abbot spoke. "Pray in this holy place. Pray for the honor of your knighthood. Pray also for humility. You have need of it."

Then he blessed them and, turning, he followed the squires from the chapel, leaving Patrick and Baldwin to the long night of prayer and silence.

Patrick stared up at the Cross and prayed with a fierce, unshaken faith. "Let me find the Cup," he pleaded. "Let it be the true Cup that You gave the Apostles to drink from at Your Last Supper. Let it be Your Grail. And let me find it for Alain's healing. Teach me humility like to Alain's so that my knighthood may not be a vain thing."

When dawn crept through the storied windows of the chapel, a priest entered to say Mass. Stiff with the long watch, and light-headed with hunger, the two boys attended the Mass, and then stumbled into the courtyard. In silence they parted and went to their separate apartments.

An hour later all those in the castle flocked to the tiltyard beyond the gates. On a dais spread with fine Arabian carpet, Sir Brian Fitz-Hubert waited to bestow knighthood on the O'Neill and on his young kinsman. For it was at Sir Brian's castle that the two boys had spent seven years in training for their knighthood, first as pages and later as squires.

Now the boys, armed at all points in their shining chain mail, were led forward. Their sponsors knelt in the dust, and fastened golden spurs to their heels. Then Patrick, putting on his sword, went and stood before Sir Brian.

"Bow the head. Receive the blow of knighthood."

Patrick bent himself forward. Sir Brian's fist struck him a great blow, and sent him reeling. The next instant the nobleman lifted him in his arms and kissed him.

"Be thou a good knight," he chanted. "Be true to thine ancient heritage, and an honor to the order to which thou art elected. Serve God."

After Baldwin had gone through the same proceedings, two magnificent war horses were led into the tiltyard. With a shout the two young knights ran forward and, despite their heavy armor, leaped astride the great animals without touching foot to stirrup.

Before Baldwin closed the visor of his helmet, he looked at Patrick and said, "Now, Sir Patrick, will I lay you in the dust."

Patrick made no answer. His servitor, Tagh Mor, handed him up a jousting lance of seasoned ashwood. He swung his shield into position, dipped his lance in salute, and wheeling, sent his steed at a gallop to the far end of the tiltyard. Like statues the two knights faced each other. When Sir Brian, acting as marshal, waved his sword, they hurtled forward, the ground echoing with the thunder of mighty hoofs. Shields swung to cover bodies, and lance points dropped as the two charged. Baldwin's lance splintered against Patrick's shield and forced his horse back on its haunches, while Patrick's lance struck his stepbrother with such force that Baldwin was lifted and flung over his horse's crupper.

Squires and servitors ran to lift Baldwin up. He was unhurt, only bruised and shaken.

Sir Brian rode into the lists. "Fairly broken, Sir Patrick," he called warmly.

Baldwin's voice was choking with rage as he cried out, "Come down and fight me on foot, fair brother, or I shall proclaim you coward."

"No, I will not fight you so," Patrick said evenly. "There is nothing dishonorable in being unhorsed. This is a joust for sport, not a battle. Moreover, our guests wait to join the hunt." He wheeled and galloped out of the tiltyard.

In the big inner court of the castle, horses were being saddled for the hunt. The kennels were in an uproar as yelping boar hounds and deer hounds were brought out by the huntsmen. Patrick was changing to a smaller, swifter horse when Baldwin rode past without so much as a glance.

"You have made yourself a mortal enemy this day," Patrick told himself bitterly. The next moment the peal of a trumpet set his blood tingling with the excitement of the chase. He snatched a boar spear from his squire, galloped across the drawbridge, and plunged into the forest.

Behind him the company of huntsmen fanned out. The yelping of the hounds and the piercing sweet notes of the hunting horns echoed and re-echoed through the forest.

Of a sudden, Patrick, hearing sounds of yelping and snarling, galloped into a clearing. There, held at bay by one of his own hounds, was the most enormous boar he had ever seen.

Patrick reined up, listening. The sounds of the hunt were fading off in the distance. Having no mind to risk injury to his horse, he dismounted, dropped his spear, and drew his sword. The boar's attention was diverted from dog to boy. Straight across the clearing it launched itself at Patrick, who sank on one knee, holding his sword level. The sword skewered the onrushing boar, as a fowl is skewered on a roasting spit. But the fury of the attack, and the weight of the beast, knocked Patrick to the ground. One of the great tusks grazed his sword arm as the dying boar flung itself across him. Then, with a convulsive shudder, it lay still, Patrick pinned beneath it.

"How is it with you now, my fair knight?"

Patrick's head jerked up, and he beheld Baldwin, an evil smile on his face.

"Seeing that I cannot rise for the weight of this beast and the weight of my armor, it is not very well with me."

Baldwin dismounted, and knelt down beside his stepbrother. Patrick saw with horror the dagger in his hand and the hatred in his eyes.

"It will be well with you soon," said Baldwin. "For it is my intention to kill you, a deed for which this noble boar must take the credit."

"Could not you and your lady mother wait until I was killed in the Holy Land, to possess yourselves of my heritage?"

At the cool mockery in Patrick's voice, the color surged into Baldwin's face. "No, I cannot wait," he said. He drew back his hand and the dagger shone in the sunlight.

But the dagger did not fall. Instead, Baldwin pitched forward, his face twisted, a black arrow quivering in his throat.

Tagh Mor, Patrick's servitor, stepped into the clearing, his longbow in his hand. "My lord, my lord, how is it with you?" he cried.

Patrick's voice was unsteady with relief as he answered. "I know not. I was very near to death but a moment since. If you will lift the boar from me, I will know better how I am."

Tagh Mor pulled the carcass of the boar from Patrick and looked with concern at the wound in his master's arm. But Patrick was staring at Baldwin. His eyes were sick.

"He is dead?" he asked.

"Even so. When I saw him kneel beside you, I thought the boar had killed you. Then I saw the dagger glint in his hand. There was no time to waste. But now his mother will want me hanged!"

"You saved my life, Tagh Mor. I am master here. You need not be afraid."

"I have never slain a man before, Lord Patrick. Let us kneel down in this place and say a prayer for his soul, for my heart is sick within me."

The two knelt and lifted their faces to Heaven. And they were kneeling there still when the rest of the hunters found them, at the going down of the sun.

196

Sunday in Assisi

"Guido! You have been fighting." Rosa spoke reprovingly.

"And on Sunday, too!"

Her brother's rapidly blackening, half-shut eye and cut lip showed that the fight had been a violent one.

Guido scowled. "Yes, and I am not going to church this afternoon," he said stubbornly.

"Not go to church!" Rosa was more shocked than ever. "Brother Francis is going to speak today. And you need his sermon. Brother Francis can make a person do anything, even behave."

"He is not going to make me do anything," Guido insisted. "He is not going to keep me from getting even with Marco." He turned swiftly, to avoid her restraining hand, and ran off toward the quiet slopes beyond the town of Assisi.

Rosa hurried on to church. It was with a sharp feeling of disappointment that she saw Brother John mount the pulpit. Brother Francis had been ill all night, he explained, and was not well enough to preach today.

When Guido reached the hills his speed slackened but his thoughts raced on. Nobody understood how unkind Marco could be nor how many little things

he did to make life difficult for Guido. Yesterday
Marco had laughed at him, and when they had
fought, Marco had gotten the best of him. Guido
was determined to get even with his enemy and
neither Rosa nor Brother Francis was going to make
him change his mind. Of that he was certain.

It was the twittering of birds that at last drew
Guido's mind away from his bitter thoughts. The
little creatures were fluttering about a man in a
coarse gray habit who sat among them scattering
crumbs. As Guido approached, the birds took no
notice of him. Suddenly tired, Guido dropped down
on the grass.

The man turned and smiled. As the boy edged a
little nearer, the man spoke.

"You love our little sisters, the birds, I see,"
he said. "But why are you here? Is it not time
for everyone to be in church?"

"I wouldn't go," Guido said sullenly. "Brother Francis was to preach. He makes you be good when you don't want to be. So I came here."

Laughter lit the eyes that met his. "Brother Francis didn't preach after all," the man said. "The Lord seemed to want Brother Francis here on the hills today."

"Are—are *you* Brother Francis?" There was dismay in Guido's voice. The man nodded.

"Well, anyhow, I'm going to get even with Marco. I don't care what you say about it." Guido spoke belligerently and waited to be rebuked.

Instead Brother Francis said, "So it is Marco who is responsible for the black eye. You must be tired. Why don't you lie on the grass and rest?"

Guido took his advice. "I gave Marco a black eye, too," he explained, "but that was not enough. He deserves much more."

When Brother Francis made no answer Guido said, "Aren't you going to preach to me?"

"Why should I? The dear Lord Himself is telling you what He wants. Why should I interfere?"

Guido put his hands under his head and looked up at the blue sky. The grass was cool and pleasant but somehow he felt uncomfortable.

The birds had been fluttering when Guido lay down but now they were still. Their little heads were cocked to one side as if they were listening to Brother Francis, who was speaking, not to Guido now, but to them. He spoke of how much God cares for each of His creatures and how those creatures should praise and love the God who made them. "Sing your songs to Him for His joy, little sisters, and for His love. The Lord Christ loved all things; He loved all men, even His enemies whom He forgave."

Guido, listening, knew there was one thing he could not do. He could not forgive Marco no matter how hard he tried. He jumped to his feet, startling the birds which rose and flew away. Without a word, Guido, too, went away, but he did not walk toward Assisi. Everyone would be coming out of church now and he did not want to see Rosa or any of them. Desiring only to get as far away as possible, he walked in the opposite direction along a path that led toward the town of Perugia.

It was not a safe way to go. For years there had been enmity between the Perugians and the people of Assisi. The path was not often used by peaceful citizens, for on it one might meet bandits or un-friendly Perugians. Too late Guido realized where he was. From nearby came the sound of voices. Silently Guido stole forward. A group of well-armed Perugians were gathered around a small fire, eating. Behind them stood a boy securely bound to a tree. The boy was Marco.

Suddenly Guido's desire
to get even with Marco
was forgotten. Marco was
no longer an enemy but
a fellow townsman who
was in danger.

Quietly Guido crept up
behind Marco and cut the
ropes that bound him to
the tree. Before the men
could scramble to their
feet in pursuit, the boys were
well on their way toward the safety of the busy
highway that lay some distance beyond the woods.

The exhausted boys soon paused for breath, but
loud shouts told them their pursuers were close
behind. As Guido tried to pull along the gasping
Marco, they heard a great bellow from the neighboring field. Saco, Master Pietro's bull, disturbed by
the noise and shouting, was lumbering across the
pasture. He was a huge beast with heavy horns and
a short temper. Guido had an idea. If Saco got out,
he would certainly complicate matters.

"We will let the bull out," Guido said. "Run to
that tree. I'll open the gate."

With difficulty Guido loosened the latch and swung
the heavy gate open, dropping out of sight behind it
as the bull rushed through.

With Marco safely up the tree, the bull's attention was drawn toward the men. He rushed after them as they scattered in all directions.

After a moment Guido called to Marco. "Come down quietly. We can take a short cut home across the field before Saco comes back." Marco dropped to the ground and the two boys started at a dog trot through the wide pasture. To Guido it seemed queer but strangely satisfying to be trotting through the sunny pasture with his former enemy. He glanced shyly at Marco and Marco, though still short of breath, smiled back warmly.

The boys had not gone far when there was a bellow close behind them. Saco had come back.

Marco ran for a tree but Guido's escape was cut off. There was nothing to which he could turn for refuge. He stopped and faced the bull. Saco pawed the ground with his head lowered. Guido wondered how long he would be able to stand and stare at the huge animal. But when he tried to step slowly backward the bull tossed his head and bellowed.

"Do not move, Guido," said a quiet voice behind him.

It was Brother Francis and he was walking straight toward the angry bull.

"Don't come any closer," Guido pleaded. "You'll be killed." Then he paused in wonder. Brother Francis was coming slowly forward, talking quietly to Saco as he did so. Soon a thin hand was on the bull's neck. The angry pawing ceased.

"Return to your rest, brother," said the gentle voice. "Lie down beneath the shade trees that God has provided, and be content." The bull hesitated, then as if obeying the command of a master, he turned and trotted away.

Not until the three were outside the pasture, and the big gate was fastened once more did Brother Francis speak.

"Let us all be brothers in Christ," he said.

The two boys looked at each other and nodded in silent agreement.

The Miracle Play

Hugh trembled with nervousness as he reported to Master William, the manager of the Miracle Play which was soon to be presented in the shadow of Lincoln Cathedral. It seemed to Hugh that there must be hundreds of guildsmen moving about the stage and dressing rooms, for each scene was to be played by a different guild.

Master William was giving last-minute directions. "Well, my boy," was his friendly greeting, "it's fortunate that Father Leo can spare you from the

204

From *Imps and Angels* by Jane Gilbert. Copyright © 1946, by Jane Gilbert. Reprinted by permission of McIntosh & Otis, Inc., New York, and the publisher, Frederick Warne & Co., Ltd., London.

choir to help us in this emergency. Now, let me show you where to stand, and what you are to do."

The first scene, Hugh knew, was to show the forming of the heavens, and among the characters were God, the Father; angels and archangels; and Lucifer with his followers who fell from Heaven because of their rebellion. Hugh was embarrassed when he learned he was to be an angel. What would the other boys say when they knew that?

"Could I be a fallen angel?" he asked timidly of Master William.

Master William had been up since long before daybreak and was beginning to show the strain of his duties. "No," he snapped, "no, we've plenty of fallen angels. You're to be just a plain angel, and no more words about it!"

Hugh was silent and listened unhappily to his instructions.

"Watch the other angels and do exactly what they do. And here are your wings." Master William went on to something more important.

Wings! These seemed almost more than Hugh could bear. As he stood with the wings in his arms, uncertain what to do next since he saw no angels to watch, a tall young guildsman noticed his drooping look and clapped him heartily on the back. "Come on over to the dressing place," he said, "and put on your white robe. I'll fix your wings on for you. Then you can help me with mine. My name is Henry. What's your name?"

If a real angel had come to his aid, Hugh could not have felt more comforted. This tall, stalwart youth was to be an angel, too! Hugh followed Henry to the hastily built shed where many other men, young and old, were moving about, talking and laughing and helping each other with their costumes. Characters from different scenes mingled together. Moses chatted with one of the shepherds; the Christ—a man chosen, Hugh knew, for his upright life—in his gilt wig and white sheepskin coat, was helping one of his tormentors put on his jacket. Pilate looked proud of his rich green cloak. Some of the actors wore masks; all had gloves on their work-worn hands.

When Hugh was dressed and his wings had been securely fastened on, he began to feel a pleasurable excitement that surprised him. All the other angels were men, and they seemed to feel no embarrassment at their rise to such high estate.

The time for the beginning of the play was very near. Crowds of townspeople and pilgrims had gathered in a wide circle about the stand where the acting was to take place. Rough benches had been constructed for dignitaries, but the greater part of the audience sat upon the ground or stood to see the play.

The boys of the choir were in their places now, at the side, where they could see but would not interfere with the view of the others. They began to sing Hugh's favorite hymn. He listened gratefully to the lines:

"Christian, never tremble,
Never be downcast,
Arm thee for the battle,
Watch and pray and fast."

Then Lucifer went up on the stage with the other angels, and Hugh followed Henry, waving his wings as he went.

Hugh had forgotten his family entirely in the excitement of being in the play, but the first person he saw from the high stand was two-year-old Barney in his kilted red tunic. Ann was holding him, but he was proving hard to manage. Between watching Henry and trying to do exactly as he did, Hugh watched Barney. He knew his little brother was never still for long, and this was his first experience of anything like the Miracle Play. Hugh tried to listen to the words spoken by Lucifer

and the others, but his eyes kept turning back to
the place where his parents stood craning their
necks to see over the crowd; then to Ann in front on
the grass with Barney. He wondered if they knew
that he was one of the angels.

Before Hugh realized it, Lucifer had fallen from
Heaven and the scene was over. Still following
Henry, Hugh left the stage and stumbled toward
the dressing room. He was soon behind the others,
for his long robe got in his way at every step and
he could not hurry. Before he reached the shed,
he noticed at one side of it an ox and a shaggy
little donkey which were to appear in the Nativity

scene. Near them stood the manger crib filled with straw and close beside it a stable lantern, through someone's forethought already lighted.

Just as Hugh, stretching and wriggling, was trying to free himself from his wings, he saw a small red figure dash toward the wooden crib. Barney had seen the donkey and was coming to it at full speed. The manger was in his path, but, with his eyes on the donkey, he did not see it. He stumbled against the light frame and it went over, knocking the lantern down with it. In an instant the straw was ablaze.

Barney's short legs were in the air, but his red tunic was caught by the flaming straw. Hugh sprang to him and, lifting his small body away from the fire, rolled him over and over upon the grass.

Barney was not hurt, but he was frightened and would have been wailing except that, with his mouth open, he forgot to cry in watching Hugh's rapid movements. Tearing off his long robe, Hugh flew to the shed where a pail of water had been placed for the actors and seized it to soak the burning straw and the dry grass that had caught around it. With swift fury he stamped out any smoldering fire that remained. All the while words raced through his mind, confused but deeply felt. "Oh, dear God," he prayed, "suppose I had not been in this spot—and I wouldn't have been here if I hadn't been an angel. Oh, God, thank You for making me an angel even if I didn't want to be one!"

Father Leo had seen the blaze and had run to seize the child while Hugh was putting out the fire. Ann appeared, gasping with sobs. Men from the dressing room came to see what was the matter, while others hurried to their places on the stage. Little Barney surveyed the scene in calm enjoyment from the height and safety of Father Leo's shoulder.

Hugh was still stamping on the grass. "We'll have to get new straw for the crib," he said, and to his surprise his voice was husky with tears. New straw—when it might have been Barney, whom no one on earth could replace!

Hugh picked up the torn robe, and went into the dressing room to find his own tunic. He did not go to join the choir. He went instead to sit close to Ann and Barney. He was still trembling a bit and he felt with comfort the sun-warmed grass under his hands.

As he sat and watched the actors in the changing scenes, Hugh saw everything with misty eyes, yet with a clearer understanding than he had ever had before. The men of Lincoln whom he had always known, were no longer ordinary, everyday guildsmen; they seemed to him to be really the figures of sacred history they stood for. All through the tremendous story he saw the care of the good God, saving His children from the flood, freeing them from slavery, forgiving their wanderings and repeated failures, finally sending His own Son to save them from their sinful mortal selves.

Gabriel and the Hour Book

King Louis XII of France thought
no gift would please his future bride,
the Lady Anne, quite so much as a
beautiful hour book. These books
were so called because in them were
written different parts of the Bible,
intended to be read at certain hours
of the day. Printing presses had
been invented only a few years and
most books were still made by the
patient labor of skillful hands. So
the king commanded the monks of
St. Martin's to do the book in the
most beautiful manner possible and
to have it finished by December.

The task was assigned to Brother
Stephen, for no other monk could
do such exquisite work. A young
peasant boy, Gabriel Viaud, became
his color grinder and helper. Every
morning Gabriel brought to the
abbey the prettiest wild flowers he
could find. These Brother Stephen
used as models when he decorated
the borders of the Lady Anne's
book. He also put in the small

212

flying creatures—butterflies and bees, scarlet ladybugs and pale green beetles whose wings looked like scraps of rainbows; and sometimes in his zeal, he even painted the little snails with their curled-up shells, and the fuzzy caterpillars that happened to come in on Gabriel's bouquets. Even these looked handsome in the gold borders when Brother Stephen got through with them.

There was much for Gabriel to do. He prepared by hand almost all of Brother Stephen's materials. Bark of the young hawthorne tree must be pounded and soaked, boiled and dried into a fine powder which would be mixed with wine when fresh ink was needed. Then there was the gold to grind and prepare; that was the hardest of all and fairly made his arms ache. Brilliant color paints were made from vegetable dyes and were held in mussel shells gathered by Gabriel from the banks of the river. Eels he must catch in the river, too; for although Brother Stephen generally used the white of

eggs for attaching the gold to his borders, yet for certain parts he preferred a glue made from the skin of an eel. This Gabriel made very well.

Sometimes Brother Stephen gave Gabriel a bit of parchment and showed him how to form letters and how to illuminate, as making the bright border decorations was called. This, too, Gabriel did very well.

Brother Stephen, like many of the monks of the time, had a good education and he was determined to share it with Gabriel.

"Ah, little one, thou hast indeed the soul of an artist!" he said. "I shall train thy hand so that it shall never know the hard toil of the peasant. Thy pen and thy brush shall earn a livelihood for thee!"

So hour after hour of the long summer evenings Brother Stephen spent teaching the lad to read and write. It was an accomplishment that few of the peasants and by no means all of the lords and ladies possessed.

In this happy manner the spring and summer wore away and the autumn came. Then Brother Stephen noticed that little by little Gabriel was beginning to look sad and distressed.

"Why, lad, whither have all thy gay spirits taken flight? Art thou ill?" he asked one morning when Gabriel seemed especially disturbed.

"Oh! Brother Stephen, we are in much trouble at home," answered Gabriel. "Count Pierre has laid a heavy tax on the peasants of his estate. The land on which we live is poor and my father was unable to raise the money Count Pierre demanded. He took all our sheep, though we begged him to have pity on us. Now he has imprisoned my father in the castle."

Brother Stephen tried to think of some way to help Gabriel, but he had no money of his own and he knew little of the ways of the outside world. There was nothing he could do except to besiege Heaven with his prayers.

At last the book was finished. As they laid the pages together in the order in which they were to go, Gabriel thought he had never seen anything half so lovely. At the beginnings of new chapters wonderful initial letters glittered in gold and colors till they looked like mosaics of precious stones, while here and there were scattered exquisite miniature pictures of saints and angels. At the very end there was yet one page more, and on it were written these words:

"I, Brother Stephen of the Abbey of St. Martins-de-Bouchage, made this book; and for every initial letter and picture and every border of flowers that I have herein wrought, I pray the Lord God to have compassion upon some one of my many sins."

As Gabriel read again this last page, it set him to thinking. All the way home he thought about Brother Stephen's prayer.

It was true that all the written and painted work had been done by Brother Stephen. But had not he, Gabriel, also done his small part to help make the book? Might not the Lord God feel kindly toward him and be willing to grant a little prayer to him, too?

While Brother Stephen was busy binding together the finished leaves, Gabriel took a piece of parchment that Brother Stephen had given him and wrote these words:

"I, Gabriel Viaud, am Brother Stephen's color grinder; and I have made the ink for this book, and the glue, and caught the eels, and ground the gold and colors, and ruled the lines, and gathered the flowers for the borders; and so I pray the Lord God will be kind and let my father out of prison in Count Pierre's castle, and tell Count Pierre to give us back our meadow and sheep, for we cannot pay the tax, and we shall all starve."

He took great pains to shape every letter perfectly. Nor did he forget that Brother Stephen had taught him always to make the word God more beautiful than the others. So he wrote that in scarlet ink and edged it with scallops and loops and little dots of blue. He very much wished for a bit of gold, but gold was precious and he had never been given any for his own.

Brother Stephen bound all the painted pages together and put on a cover of violet velvet exquisitely embroidered in pearls and gold by the nuns of a nearby convent. The cover was fastened with clasps of wrought gold, set with amethysts. It was a royal gift, worthy of any queen. After it had been duly admired by all the monks in the abbey, it was wrapped up in a piece of soft, rich silk and laid on a shelf to wait till the next morning, when a messenger would come for it and take it to the Lady Anne.

That evening, when no one was watching, Gabriel unwrapped the book and put his page next to Brother Stephen's. In due time the Lady Anne, coming upon Gabriel's little prayer in the book, was deeply touched. She wrote to the king and asked if he could not see to it that Count Pierre set the boy's father free.

This King Louis determined to do, for he was a just and kind-hearted monarch, and during his reign did much to lighten the taxes and oppression of the peasant-folk; moreover, it gave him great pleasure to grant any wish of the Lady Anne, whom he loved dearly. So after some investigation Gabriel's father was released. The king himself bought the land on which the Viaud cottage stood and sent a deed for it to Gabriel's father. But, the messenger insisted, the king did not want anyone except the lad's father and mother, not even Gabriel himself, to know how it had all come about.

For King Louis declared that he himself did not deserve any thanks, but that the good God had only chosen the Lady Anne and himself and Count Pierre (though the latter did not know it) as the means of answering Gabriel's prayer.

The University at Krakow

It was late in the year 1493, and the University of Krakow was opening for the winter term.

Of all the spectacles of the Middle Ages there were few that equaled in color and spirit the festive days of university folk, for learning was much honored. On this October day church bells pealed, trumpets sounded, royal folk left off affairs of state, and apprentices forgot their quarrels to celebrate the opening of the university.

Suddenly the air was cut by the brisk notes of a trumpet call. It was the Heynal, played for the first of four times in the high tower of the church of Panna Marya. Each time the call ended on a broken note, and when the note faded away for the last time, the whole city seemed to arouse itself and leap into a frenzy of excitement and action.

"They are coming! They are coming!"

Onlookers pressed forward into the very streets where horsemen of the king's guard were dashing back and forth to clear the way. Folk scampered back shrieking, to join the thousands who were gathered in the narrow side streets. From peasants' homes, from small towns, from distant cities even, people had come to gaze on the magnificent spectacle. The housetops were lined, windows were crowded, balconies were crushingly full.

From *From Star to Star* by Eric P. Kelly. Copyright, 1942, 1944, by Eric P. Kelly. Published by J. B. Lippincott Company.

With a fluttering of black and white garments,
a group of choristers appeared, singing the university hymn in Latin. They came slowly and with
measured steps.

Behind them came, on foot and in robes that
equaled the richness of coronation dress, His Majesty
the king to honor the university which held high
rank among all the schools of Europe.

The cheering rose in a great tumult. The king!
The king himself! In his train came a company
of knights, soldiers, and servitors. Then, elevated
upon his throne, clad in robes of red, came the
Prince-Cardinal, brother to the king, and president
of the university. Thy blessing, Eminence! Heads
bowed at the Prince-Cardinal's uplifted fingers,
and lips murmured a prayer.

Next were the monks. Then in order of rank came the professors and masters of the university.

All at once a cry of welcome went up from the crowd. The students were coming. Out of their dwellings they poured by the hundreds, some in fine gowns, others in poor ones. The older students in front kept some order and rhythm in their steps, but they talked constantly and shook hands in all directions. Behind them the younger boys made almost no attempt to keep in line.

The procession ended at the church of St. Ann, where the Cardinal turned and blessed the crowd once more. When the church door had closed behind the dignitaries, students began shouting, and the crowd swarmed into the street. Bells pealed and snatches of song rang out in celebration. The college year had begun.

A quiet observer of all this was a country boy in hunting leathers and pointed cap. He was Roman Stan, who had entered the city the previous night, just before the closing of the gates. He had made his way to the Cloth Hall in the Central Market, and there beneath the stall counter of a kindly tradesman he had spent the night. In his mind now there was just one idea, to enroll himself in the lowest class of the university. He had only enough money for the first fee. A student's gown was needed, too, but it was said that used gowns might be had for hire, or for work. As for his food and lodging, perhaps there might be a chance to earn those in one of the colleges where the housekeeping duties were performed by poor students.

Books the boy did not hope to possess, for although a few books were being printed in the fifteenth century, they were still not plentiful. Students waited in line, sometimes for hours, just to consult those belonging to the masters.

Young though he was, and almost penniless in this great medieval city, Roman Stan was not discouraged, for the stimulation of the place raised his spirits to the skies. The city itself was not unfriendly. Everyone spoke kindly. Even the buildings and churches that he knew so well from story and legend—for who in Poland does not know Krakow—seemed to offer him friendly protection.

So, resolved to register himself as soon as the authorities returned from the services, he roamed about the city. He soon found himself in a street known in later years as the Street of the Pigeons. Now it was a nesting place of alchemists and others who practiced in various branches of the Black Art. The dark and somber thoroughfare seemed to be one mass of strange signs and magic symbols. Unconsciously, Roman quickened his steps, for he feared this mysterious neighborhood.

All at once he was collared from behind.

Turning with a shudder, he faced a group of ten
or twelve youths. They were students apparently,
for some of them wore gowns. Shabby gowns they
were, moth-eaten and bedraggled, but gowns for all
that. He felt sure he was among his own kind.

"Are you a student?" asked the youth who had
seized him. "Where is your gown?"

"I am not registered yet," answered Roman.

"What luck, friends," shouted the youth, turning
to his companions. "Here's *Bejaunus*."

"You mistake, my name is Roman."

A roar of laughter went up. Roman had not
recognized the name used to ridicule new students!

"Let me go," he cried.

"He doesn't like us," said one.

"He wants his mother," said another.

The next thing Roman knew, the whole company was pushing and shoving him forward. It was useless to fight, and he had too much pride to cry out.

The youths hustled him down a flight of stairs into a cellar eating place. A stout woman, grinning broadly, flapped her apron and kept asking, "What will you have? What will you have?"

"Here's a *Bejaunus*," said the first youth. "A wild *Bejaunus* just out of the woods. He's going to buy us something to eat. Aren't you, *Bejaunus*?"

Roman thought of his few pieces of copper and his heart sank. "I would gladly," he said, bowing, "but my funds are short."

"His funds are short! Think of that!"

Roman had heard nothing of students' pranks; he had thought of the university as a place where men were interested only in things of the mind. He looked at the faces about him, most of them pinched by hunger. Well, he thought, if this was to come, it was to come. He would see it through.

His tormentor, snatching Roman's pouch, spread the few coins it contained on the table.

"Here's enough for eat and drink," he cried. "What will you have, brothers?"

"The money was intended for my fee," Roman tried to explain. But the woman had quickly

224

gathered up the money and was beginning to serve each student with whatever he called for.

As Roman stood by helpless, the students began singing and eating the meal his scanty funds had provided. In a short time the feast had come to an end and the woman was urging them to leave.

"*Ave atque vale*," shouted the youths as they departed. "See you again, *Bejaunus*."

Roman stumbled out into the street sick at heart. The city which had been so gay in the morning was suddenly gray and dismal. He walked aimlessly, not knowing where to go. Then seeing the open door of Panna Marya Church, he went in and settled himself wearily in a pew. People were stirring all about him—peasants from the market, students, mothers with children. Soon an old man came and began to light the candles on the High Altar.

As Roman watched and prayed, a strange new feeling of peace came over him. He thought once more of his eagerness to learn the wisdom of the ancients and the laws of his land. No doubt those other boys, beneath their boisterousness, had the same yearning for knowledge which had brought him to Krakow; else why were they here?

Ashamed at his recent weakness, he arose from his pew and left the church. He was determined to find some work by means of which he could earn enough to pay his first fee in the university.

Cream of the Jesters

When Philip Neri walked abroad
Beside the Tiber, praising God,
They say he was attended home
By half the younger set of Rome.

Knight, novice, scholar, boisterous boy,
They followed after him with joy,
To nurse his poor and break his bread
And hear the funny things he said.

For Philip Neri (by his birth
A Florentine) believed in mirth,
Holding that virtue took no harm
Which went with laughter arm-in-arm.

Two books he read with most affection—
The Gospels and a joke collection;
And sang hosannas set to fiddles
And fed the sick on soup and riddles.

So when the grave rebuke the merry,
Let them remember Philip Neri
(Fifteen-fifteen to ninety-five),
Who was the merriest man alive,
Then, dying at eighty or a bit,
Became a saint by Holy Wit.

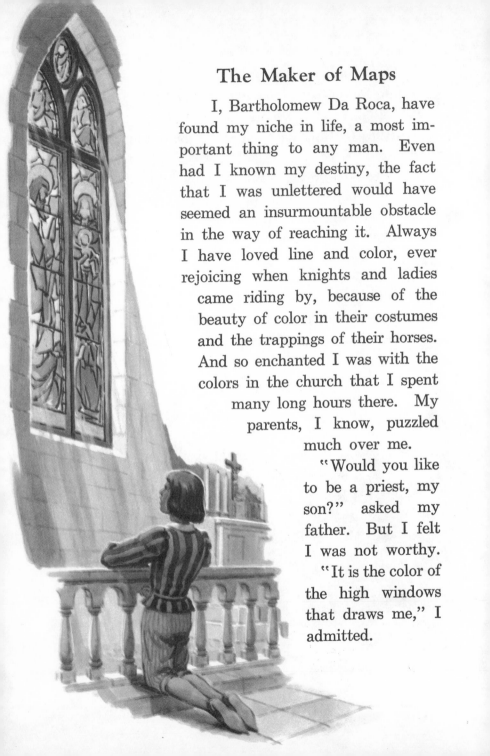

The Maker of Maps

I, Bartholomew Da Roca, have found my niche in life, a most important thing to any man. Even had I known my destiny, the fact that I was unlettered would have seemed an insurmountable obstacle in the way of reaching it. Always I have loved line and color, ever rejoicing when knights and ladies came riding by, because of the beauty of color in their costumes and the trappings of their horses. And so enchanted I was with the colors in the church that I spent many long hours there. My parents, I know, puzzled much over me.

"Would you like to be a priest, my son?" asked my father. But I felt I was not worthy.

"It is the color of the high windows that draws me," I admitted.

"Color," said my father thoughtfully. "Perhaps you would like to learn weaving and dyeing with your Uncle Pedro."

I thought I would, but I was poor at the weaving and my uncle was not a patient man. After the long hours at the loom I often sought the shipyard where my brothers worked as carpenters. There was line here, as well as color—the sweep of the hulls, the slope of the masts, and the coats of arms with their strange devices. Sometimes I was allowed to help with the mixing of paints. Then one of the painters left and I was allowed to work in his place, making simple designs. Most of the painters had a tracing to follow, but I was soon drawing my own designs. My brothers were quite proud of me.

One day the master painter pointed to a fine new sailing vessel that was near completion.

"I wish you to make a scroll for her, of your own designing. The owner is enamored of all these tales of wondrous Cathay, and he desires dragons to be entwined with the scrollwork. The figurehead will be a Chinese lady—it is being done by a most skillful carver. If you make a success of the scroll, perhaps you can paint the figurehead."

To paint a figurehead! Who could ask for more! The owner was pleased with my scroll and insisted on paying extra for it. And, of course, I could paint the figurehead.

How strange life is! It was that extra pay which changed the course of mine.

It took me into a street I had never entered before, where I was told there was a fine shop. I wished to buy my mother a little crucifix of real gold. I found a beautifully wrought piece and a leather box to hold it. So delighted was I that I took a wrong turn and came upon a very old house with a great window full of wonderful maps. As I stood looking at the maps, and wondering into what strange seas my figurehead would go, an old man came to the window, smiled, and beckoned me in.

What a place that was! Maps covered the walls, and on a huge table there was another map, just in outline. Beside it were many quills in a jar, and little dishes of colored inks and paints.

"I saw your interest," said the old man kindly, "and I wondered if, perchance, you were seeking occupation. I am growing old and there are many commissions—every patron demanding a new map as our horizons widen. I sorely need a young apprentice to help me."

I explained—though, I think, with modesty—about the scroll, and the figurehead I had still to paint, but so eager was I to work in that place that I plunged on. "I am not always working," I said. "I could come sometimes. But I fear my assistance would be limited, for I cannot—I cannot read or write."

It was the first time I had ever cared about not knowing how to read and write. It had never seemed a need in my humble life.

My mother wept with joy over the golden crucifix but chided me for spending so much. "You should save your money, my son. Some day there will be a lovely girl."

I laughed. I was far too busy to be thinking of girls.

Whenever I was not working at the shipyard, and sometimes after hours, when I was, I worked with old Cabral, the maker of maps. After we had finished some piece of work, he would ask me to stay for a bite to eat. And then he would explain the maps on the walls to me.

"Not all of these are mine, lad. Some are my father's and my grandfather's before me. Those early ones of my grandfather's have islands upon them never to this day really discovered. We may conclude that they never existed save in the imagination of man.

"As to the Sea of Darkness, no one knew what lay beyond it. Ships stayed near the coast, but sailors told strange and dreadful tales about that unknown sea and its monsters.

"My father told me once of my grandfather's problems in picturing the sea serpent. Little was

known of it, but well-paying patrons wished the terrors of the Sea of Darkness shown in detail, and to make a handsome map one must fill in some vacant spaces. After all, the New World was almost unknown, and Asia was known imperfectly. My grandfather consulted many learned men regarding the sea serpent. Some believed it did not exist, others were merely uncertain. Almost no one would admit having seen one.

"I am glad my grandfather lived to record the voyage of that great admiral Columbus. My own father's day was almost too full of events. He had to make one new map after another. Spain conquered Mexico and Peru with their endless treasure. Balboa fought through the jungles of Panama seeking Asia, but found instead that greatest of seas, the blue Pacific.

"By the time I was old enough to make maps Magellan's men had sailed across the Pacific back to Europe. No more arguments now about the earth's being round!"

A few weeks later old Cabral said to me, "I wish you could read and write. My old eyes grow weary of the lettering and with your fine hand for a line or a scroll you could easily acquire the graceful sweep of the letters. I have an idea, if it does not displease you. My granddaughter will teach you to read."

I did not wholly like the idea of being taught by a woman, but I was eager to learn. It was arranged for me to come two evenings a week.

I was picking out letters on a map when the door opened and old Cabral spoke to me. "Bartholomew, your teacher, Viana Cabral."

So long as life remains I will never forget my first sight of her. She was slim and small as a child and she had on a dress of old-fashioned cut, green-blue like the sea and like her own eyes; and her hair was black and shone like a bird's wings.

I had not the wits to speak, but she smiled and pointed to a little table with a candle upon it. She was so beautiful in the candlelight I feared I could not even learn the alphabet for looking at her.

But in a short time I had learned it, and she taught me to read, mostly from the old maps, which made it easier. The writing was not too hard, for I liked much to form the shapes of letters.

"You have read everything on the old maps," she announced one evening. "Now you must have books."

But it was some time before I could have any more lessons, for there was a new vessel needing a scroll

which I must design at night. There was a figurehead to be painted too, of a girl as slim as Viana and
much like her. I sought the owner of the ship, a
tall man, richly dressed, his fingers stiff with many
rings.

"If this figurehead is of your wife or a daughter,"
I ventured, "would you allow me to see the coloring?"

"My wife and my daughters," he replied sourly,
"are the shape and size of wine casks, and with swart
complexions. Paint this figure as you choose—as
the most lovely woman you have ever seen, my lad."

So I painted the figurehead with skin the color of
apple blossoms and eyes and dress the blue-green of
the sea, and black hair that shone like a bird's wings.

The owner praised me much and gave me a golden bracelet set with stones the color of sea water.

"For your sweetheart, young man," he said. "For no man could paint a figurehead like that were he not in love."

I suppose I had always known, but had not dared to know.

I went early for my lesson that night and sought out old Cabral. He smiled at me and at my stammering tale of unworthiness, and fears that Viana would only laugh at me.

"My old eyes fail me, but I can still see more than you young folk. She will not laugh."

When I gave the bracelet to Viana, she uttered a cry of delight. "But you should not give it to me," she protested.

"You have been teaching me all these months," I said lamely, "and it is the color of your dress."

"I will wear it tonight," she said, "but I cannot keep it. You should save it for—for—"

"I have no choice," I said, boldly now. "It was given to me for my sweetheart and for no one else." She looked at me long and hard. Then she held out her slim arm and I clasped the bracelet upon it.

So you see why, today, I am so contented a man. Old Cabral left me his business, and commissions pour in. I have just started work on a map showing the New World. It is a very handsome map, for it

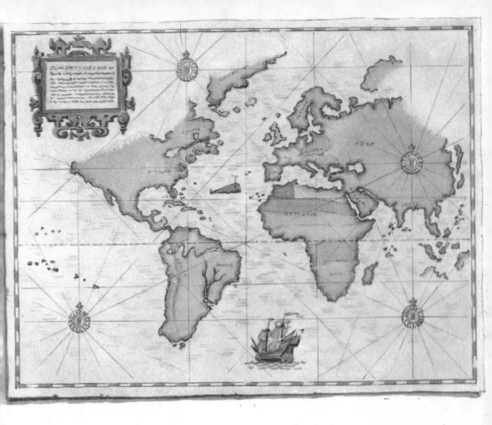

bears many coats of arms; far north that of France;
the British lion in that land they call New England;
south of that there is the claim of the Netherlands,
on the island of Manhattan; farther south is the
British lion again, in the country of Virginia. Spain
still holds the land of Florida and indefinite spaces
to the west.

The ocean once called the Sea of Darkness is a
highroad today. Some inland waterway to Asia is
still sought, but no man is sure of the width of this
strange New World. I hope I may live to know.

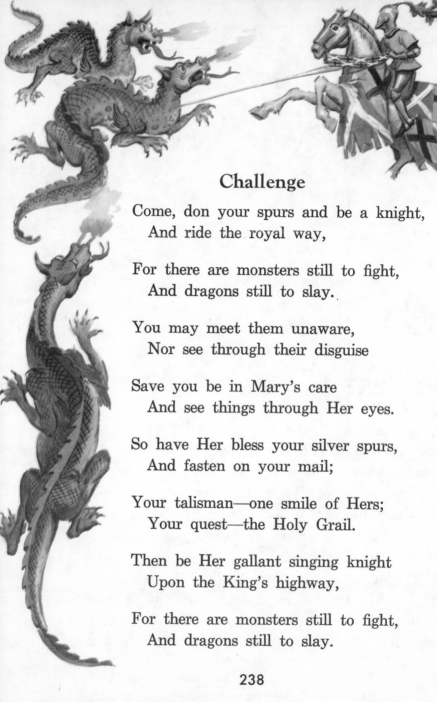

Challenge

Come, don your spurs and be a knight,
  And ride the royal way,

For there are monsters still to fight,
  And dragons still to slay.

You may meet them unaware,
  Nor see through their disguise

Save you be in Mary's care
  And see things through Her eyes.

So have Her bless your silver spurs,
  And fasten on your mail;

Your talisman—one smile of Hers;
  Your quest—the Holy Grail.

Then be Her gallant singing knight
  Upon the King's highway,

For there are monsters still to fight,
  And dragons still to slay.

238

"Challenge" by Sister M. Philip, C.S.C., used by permission of "The Young Catholic Messenger," Geo. A. Pflaum, Publisher, Dayton, Ohio, and the Sisters of the Holy Cross, Saint Mary's Convent, Notre Dame, Indiana.

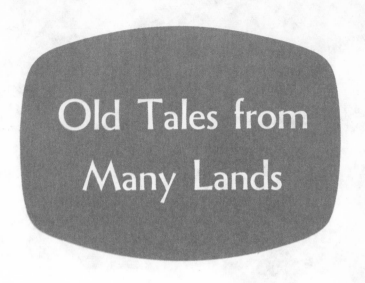

Old Tales from Many Lands

The King's Rice Pudding

Once upon a time, long, long ago, the king of the Netherlands sent word to the little village of Onstwedde that he would pay it a royal visit within a few days.

Since the king was beloved by all his subjects, the people of Onstwedde naturally were very much pleased by the good tidings. But they wondered how they could show the king that they appreciated this honor. They would have liked to present him with a regal gift. Yet they were not rich enough to buy anything suitable. Besides, the king already had everything in the world that he wanted.

Adapted by permission of the publisher, J. B. Lippincott Company, from "The King's Rijstepap," from *Picture Tales from Holland*, by Johan Hart. Copyright, 1935, by J. B. Lippincott Company.

The burgomaster called his villagers together to discuss the matter. No one, however, could suggest anything that was considered satisfactory. At last the burgomaster gave up all hope of finding an answer to this grave problem. Then suddenly he himself had a brilliant idea for a gift.

"I know what we can do!" he cried. "You are all aware that our village is famous for a rice pudding that is beyond compare. We are unable to give the king anything of great value. So let us each offer him a bowl of our finest rice pudding."

The villagers applauded the idea. Accordingly, the town crier made the announcement in the market square. Every village man's wife was to prepare a bowl of the most delicious rice pudding she could make, for presentation to the king.

At once the good women hurried to their kitchen cupboards to collect all the necessary ingredients: rice, milk, eggs, and sugar. Then they set to work most industriously.

On the morning of the king's arrival in the village all the men met at the town hall. Each had a big bowl of rice pudding in his hands.

Now these men were just simple folk. They had never before been in the presence of royalty. So they shyly asked their burgomaster for guidance in making the presentation of the rice pudding to His Majesty, the king.

"I'll go in and offer my bowl of pudding first," the burgomaster said importantly. "You just follow me and do exactly as I do."

With great pomp and dignity the burgomaster set out for the inn where the king was staying. One by one the village men with their bowls got in line and followed the burgomaster.

Everything went well until they entered the hall where the king sat. Then the burgomaster's feet slipped. Zip! Away he went, sliding across the waxed floor and tumbling flat on his stomach. Up flew the bowl from his hands! It landed in a hundred pieces at the king's feet and spattered rice pudding on the royal garments.

The other men thought that this was a strange way to welcome royalty. But they remembered their burgomaster's instructions to do exactly as he did.

Each man in turn fell on his stomach, throwing his bowl of rice pudding at the king's feet.

The burgomaster grew red with anger. He bellowed at the man next to him, "What a dunderhead you are!"

The villager was confused but agreeable. He called out good-naturedly, "What a dunderhead you are!"

That was too much for the flustered burgomaster. Scrambling to his feet, he pounced upon his neighbor and soundly boxed the poor fellow's ears.

That man immediately turned around and boxed the next man's ears. Thus it went on down the whole line of men. Some of them did not take the whacking in a suitable spirit. Soon a rough-and-tumble scuffle was going on right in the presence of the royal visitor.

At first the king was very much surprised and more than a little indignant at such outrageous behavior. But in a moment he began to laugh. The sight of all those angry village men spattered with creamy rice pudding and rolling furiously about on the floor seemed ridiculously funny to him. He laughed and laughed until big tears began to roll down his face.

Finally the burgomaster caught the man who was nearest him by the collar and hauled him out of the room.

Immediately the others jumped up and followed the burgomaster, who was thoroughly ashamed of himself and the ignorant villagers. But the king and his noblemen left the village still chuckling to themselves. "Seldom in all my long travels through the Netherlands have my subjects entertained me so well," the king said. "When I arrive at my palace, I shall send back a purse of gold coins to the burgomaster. He can divide it among the villagers to show them how much I appreciate the good time I had at Onstwedde."

244

Thor's Unlucky Journey

Thor, the red-headed god of thunder, not only was very strong but also had two mighty weapons. The greater of these was his hammer. When it was hurled against an enemy of the gods, the foe was immediately destroyed. Once its work was done, the hammer returned of its own accord to Thor's hand. In addition, the god owned a magic belt that doubled his natural strength.

For a long time Thor had been eager to visit the dark and icy land of the giants. He wished to show their wicked ruler how great and powerful were the gods. For this journey Thor wanted a brave and daring comrade. Therefore, he chose Loki, the handsome god of fire; and off they set on their long journey.

Thor's two strong goats pulled his chariot through the gates of Asgard, the home of the gods. Quickly the goats raced out of sight as the other gods cheered the travelers on.

From *Adventures with the Giants*, by Catharine F. Sellew, by permission of Little, Brown & Co. Copyright, 1950, by Catharine F. Sellew.

All day long they traveled with the swiftness of the winds. By the time the sun had disappeared behind the mountains, the two gods were near the edge of the giant king's domain. Before them was a tiny cottage where a poor peasant family lived. When the chariot stopped, the peasants welcomed the red-bearded Thor and his handsome friend and invited them in to spend the night.

The mother set a small cheese and a loaf of barley bread on the table.

"We have very little to offer," said the father. "But we are glad to share it with you."

Loki's eyes twinkled as he looked at Thor. He knew that the thunder god could swallow both the bread and cheese in one gulp. Thor laughingly said that he would provide fresh meat. Whereupon, he slew his two goats and added them to the meal. The peasants gasped in wonder.

"Eat all you wish," roared Thor, "but see that you don't break any of the bones. When you have eaten all the meat off them, toss the bones over on the goatskins."

The poverty-stricken peasants ate ravenously and threw aside the bones. Unfortunately, the son of the family chanced to break one of the small, fragile leg bones.

In the morning when Thor awoke, he waved his magic hammer over the skins upon which the bare bones lay. Up sprang the goats, alive again and ready to pull the chariot. But alas, one goat had a slight limp.

"Someone disobeyed my order!" thundered Thor, angry sparks flying from his red beard.

The peasants trembled. They now realized that their guests were gods. The son, Thialfi, fell to his knees and begged Thor's forgiveness.

Angry as he was, the god could not bring himself to harm the youth before him. Sternly he said, "To win my forgiveness, you and your sister, Roskva, must come with us and be our servants. We will leave my two goats in the care of your parents. Make haste! We must be off!"

Thor led the way on foot. Soon the travelers entered a land where the mist lay so thick that no one could guess what hour of the day or night it was. But after a while Thor declared that it was time to seek a place to rest.

"Look ahead!" cried the mighty thunder god as he groped his way forward. He pointed toward a dark mass that loomed in the mist. Going closer, the others saw what seemed to be an odd-shaped house. A doorway that filled the front part was wide open. At the side of the house a round tower was leaning at a queer angle.

Boldly Thor led the others inside. There was no fire, not even a hearth on which to build one.

Neither was there any furniture. But the place
seemed safe. The travelers threw themselves on
the floor and soon fell fast asleep. After a while
they all woke with a start. The ground was trembling. The whole house was quaking, and a great
rumbling and roaring could be heard. Eventually
the disturbance began to diminish.

"I saw a small room leading off this hall," Thor
told the others. "The three of you may finish the
night in there. I shall guard the doorway."

Soon the three were in deep slumber. The next
morning they were awakened by Thor's laughter.
"Ho, ho! I found out about that earthquake," he
chuckled. "Do you realize where we are?"

The others shook their heads, staring at Thor
in wonderment.

Thor threw back his head and roared with good
humor. "We've been sleeping in the thumb of a
giant's mitten! The giant was sleeping outside it.
That roaring, rumbling, and shaking was his snoring. I've been talking to him, and he has agreed to
show us the way to the gate of the giants' city.
Come out and meet him yourselves."

Thor led his friends
outside. Before them
stood two gigantic
boots; and up,

into the mist stretched
the giant's tall figure.
His face appeared as a
gray blur to the four
who stood like dwarfs
below him.

"These people are my
friends," Thor shouted
to the giant. "Lead on
and we will follow."

The giant bent down
to pick up his mitten
and a knapsack. Then
he started ahead into the
wispy clouds, with the
gods and their two serv-
ants following at the
heels of his huge boots.

For a whole day they
traveled on through the
misty land. At last the
giant stopped and lay
down upon the ground.
He tossed his knapsack
to Thor and said, "Eat
all you like of the food
inside." Immediately,
the giant fell asleep.

Thor and Loki pulled and tugged at the straps that tied the bag. Then they tried to cut the thick leather, but nothing could rip the tough rawhide. Finally they gave up and went to bed hungry.

But even sleep seemed impossible. The giant's snores were louder than the night before. Thor was incensed at such rudeness. He was sure that the giant had known they would not be able to get food from the knapsack, and now was deliberately keeping them awake. It was time, Thor decided, to teach the uncivil monster a lesson.

Whereupon, the god drew his great hammer from his belt and smote the sleeper on the forehead. The giant winced and turned over.

"Was that a leaf that fell upon my head?" he murmured and resumed his snoring.

Thor glowered at the giant's monstrous body. Then once again he raised his hammer and hurled it with all his might at the prostrate form. Again the giant stirred in his sleep.

"A piece of bark must have fallen on me," he complained.

Once more Thor threw his hammer. This time the giant sat up. "It's quite late at night for birds to be gathering twigs for nests," he grumbled. "But I'm sure that a twig just fell on my head. Well, there still is time to get more sleep." Onto his side he rolled with a wide yawn.

When morning came, the giant pointed to a road leading straight to the palace of his king. Then he faded away. Suddenly out of the silver mist a gleaming castle appeared ahead of the two gods and their servants. It was made of blocks and pillars of ice. The roof of dazzling white snow glittered like diamonds. Across the entrance were strong metal bars. But big as Loki and Thor were, they managed to squeeze through the spaces between the bars. Thus the gods entered the castle and stood before the king of the giants.

The mighty king was sitting on a throne at one end of a tremendous hall filled with other giants.

"So you are the gods I have been hearing about," the king bellowed. "How small you are! Surely creatures so small cannot do all that we are told you do!"

His loud laugh rang from the high rafters. It echoed a hundred times throughout the palace hall.

"How small! How small!" resounded from every corner of the room.

Then Loki stepped forward. "We may not be so big as you, but we are wiser and more clever. We can do all that you can do—and do it better."

"Oho," mocked the king. "We will see about that." Leaning back on his throne, he slyly said, "Let us have a contest to prove whether or not your boast is true. What do you wish to do?"

Loki's face was red with anger. But his stomach was empty and aching from a day without food. With great relish he declared that he could eat more than any giant and twice as fast.

"Very well," said the king. At once he ordered the cook to match his appetite against Loki's. A long, narrow, wooden dish was placed on the floor. The dish, which stretched across the width of the vast hall, was filled with hot meat stew.

Loki sat at one end of the wooden dish, and the giant cook at the other. The tempting smell of the food made the hungry Loki grin and forget the jeering giants. At the king's signal, the cook and Loki began to gorge themselves.

Finally Loki came to the center of the dish and looked up in triumph. But, alas, the cook had long since eaten his portion, including the meat bones and his half of the wooden dish. The giants' roars of laughter brought Loki leaping to his feet. He strode over to Thor.

"There's some strange magic power in this," he whispered. "If these giants are so mighty, why do they fear us when we are in Asgard?"

"I do not understand," said Thor with a scowl.

"Now," called the king, "perhaps you can excel at something else."

"My thirst is never quenched," cried Thor. "In one gulp I'll drain your largest drinking vessel."

At once an immense drinking horn was brought in. It was filled to the brim with rich brown ale. Thor took the horn in his strong hands. Throwing back his head, he drew a deep breath. Then he lifted the horn to his lips and drank and drank. Thick veins bulged out on his forehead. His face grew redder and redder until it turned purple, but still he drank. Loki and the peasants looked on with pride. The giants only chortled.

Then with a gasp Thor lowered the horn from his mouth. Everyone crowded forward to look into the horn. Lo! the ale had gone down only an inch.

"Try again," urged the king. "Our good drinkers can empty the horn the first time. Moderately thirsty ones need to take two gulps."

So Thor tried again. But he barely lowered the level of the ale in the great horn. A third time he did no better. Finally he sat down in defeat.

Up jumped the gods' servant boy, Thialfi. He challenged any giant to a foot race. One of the young giants rose, and everyone went forth to a great bare field. When the king gave the word, the runners raced around the field like the wind. Thor and Loki were surprised at Thialfi's grace and speed. Yet the giant soon forged ahead of the lad. Once more the giants were the winners.

Thor still refused to give up. With his hand on his magic belt, he suggested a wrestling match.

"Well," exclaimed the giant king, "I admire your courage; but for one of your small size, it is a foolish challenge."

"Do you refuse?" the thunder god cried in fury.

"Not at all," the king replied. "But I can let no one stronger than my ancient nurse wrestle with you. I should not like to see any violence done to one of the mighty gods while in our midst."

Thor's hair flamed even brighter than usual. Such insults were too much to bear. But there was nothing to do but wrestle with the grizzled old woman.

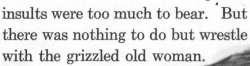

The old nurse and the great thunder god tussled and rolled in the center of the hall until at last Thor was pinned to the floor. He had lost the match.

Still determined to do something successfully, Thor suggested proving his strength by weight lifting. At this the giants' cat was brought into the room. It was such a big cat that it looked like a tiger, but Thor tightened his belt with satisfaction. He knew that he had lifted heavier weights than this cat. He bent over the animal's back and put both arms around its body. He heaved with all his might, expecting to toss it as high as the roof. But it did not move. Thor tugged and pushed and pulled. Still the cat did not budge.

"It's bewitched," Loki muttered.

Thor agreed, yet he determined to try once more. Gritting his teeth, he gave a tremendous heave and managed to lift one paw from the floor.

"You see!" cried the king. "We have proved our power. Perhaps after this you gods will speak of us with respect. In the morning I will conduct you to the edge of my realm and see you off on your way to Asgard."

The next morning the giant king confronted the gods at the sea's edge. He had an admiring look in his eyes. "Thor and Loki," he said, "now that you are leaving, I have something to confess. If I had ever guessed your strength and courage, I would not have let you enter my kingdom. I was the giant whose snores woke you. I was the one who led you to my own gates."

The king turned to the red-haired god. "When you, Thor, struck me with your hammer, you hit a mountain instead of my forehead. I feared your hammer, and by magic I placed an invisible mountain between it and me."

Then the king looked at Loki. "The cook who ate faster than you was Wild Fire, which destroys all. Your servant lad ran a race with Thought, which travels more swiftly than any runner. The horn from which Thor drank was connected with the sea, which nobody can empty. My nurse was Old Age, whom none can defeat. The cat was the evil snake that twists itself around the world. When Thor managed to lift one of its feet, we giants were terrified. We feared that he would loosen the horrible creature and bring destruction down upon us all. Only by magic and trickery were we enabled to delude and overcome you."

At this admission Thor roared with rage and raised his hammer. But the mist had now grown thicker, and the giant king was invisible.

"So there was magic!" Loki cried.

But Thor said nothing. He stared at the shore of the sea. Several feet above the place where the waves washed the sand was a dark wet line. It marked where the water had once been.

Thor smiled. He knew now that he had drunk well from the great horn. He had done better than any other god could have done and far, far better than any giant. He was content at last to return to Asgard.

The Fox and the Grapes

A MORAL TALE FOR THOSE WHO FAIL

One summer's day a Fox was passing through
An orchard; faint he was and hungry, too.
When suddenly his keen eye chanced to fall
Upon a bunch of grapes above the wall.
"Ha! Just the thing!" he said. "Who could
   resist it!"
He eyed the purple cluster—jumped—and
   missed it!
"Ahem!" he coughed. "I'll take more careful aim,"
And sprang again. Results were much the same,
Although his leaps were desperate and high.
At length he paused to wipe a tearful eye,
And shrug a shoulder. "I am not so dry,
And lunch is bound to come within the hour ...
Besides," he said, "I'm sure those grapes
   were sour."

The Moral Is: We somehow want the peach
That always dangles just beyond our reach;
Until we learn never to be upset
With what we find too difficult to get.

From *Rainbow in the Sky* edited by Louis Untermeyer. Copyright, 1935, by Harcourt, Brace and Company, Inc.

Pandora

Epimetheus, one of the last Titans on the earth, was very lonely. Day after day he wandered about, utterly disconsolate. Finally word of his complaints reached Jupiter, ruler of the gods.

"It is time to send him a wife," Jupiter decided. He therefore ordered Vulcan, the god of the forge, to obtain a wife for Epimetheus.

Up to this time there had been no woman on the earth. So the goddesses were greatly interested in the undertaking. They watched Vulcan, eager to see what he would do. Not far from the summit of the mountain on which the gods lived was a bubbling fountain. Here Vulcan, the black-browed god of craftsmen, scooped up clay from the rim of the fountain. Using this clay, he molded the form of a woman.

"Let us help," the goddesses cried. And they began to bring gifts to the woman of clay.

"You shall be wise," said Minerva, the goddess of wisdom. As she spoke, she fastened ornaments of precious jewels around the figure's waist.

"You shall be beautiful," promised Venus, smiling at the statue.

Ceres, the goddess of the harvest, hung lovely garlands about the neck of the statue and then stood back to admire her handiwork.

At that moment Mercury appeared with a large carved box in his arms. "I, too, must bestow a gift," exclaimed the messenger god. "You shall be full of curiosity." Mercury touched the figure's lips with a wand. "Speak, Pandora," he said, "for that shall be your name. It means 'Gift of All.'"

At once the clay statue came to life. She moved about so gracefully and spoke so meekly that the goddesses were charmed with her. Then Mercury, still bearing the box, put his hand upon her arm; and together they floated away.

From the skies Jupiter had watched these proceedings with great satisfaction. He bore a grudge against the men of the earth. To get revenge, he had given Mercury instructions regarding the box. Now, as Jupiter thought of his cunning plot, he gloated. The gift of curiosity that had been bestowed upon Pandora would further his malicious plan.

Meanwhile, Mercury and Pandora had neared the home of Epimetheus.

"This box was lent by Jupiter," Mercury told Pandora, handing it to her. "You and Epimetheus must be very careful never to open it."

"Not even for a tiny peep?" Pandora asked.

"Not even so much as one hair's-breadth," the messenger god insisted.

"Why not?" Pandora inquired in a sulky tone.

"Because it is forbidden," the god replied sternly. But in his eyes there was an unmistakably sly look.

The moment that Epimetheus beheld the beautiful Pandora, he was delighted with her. When he was told about the box, he set it in his house. Then he gave his solemn promise never to permit anyone to open it.

But Pandora made no such promise, and as the days passed, she found herself thinking more and more often about the mysterious box. To begin with, Mercury had aroused her curiosity concerning its contents. And then Epimetheus never let her forget the fact that they were forbidden to open the box. Often when he left her, she would hear the quick thud of his footsteps along the wooded path as he came rushing back. In another moment he would appear and say, "I forgot to remind you. Whatever you do today, do not under any circumstances open that box!"

One day when Epimetheus had left after his usual warning, Pandora was alone in the house.

"What shall I do this morning?" she asked herself. "Shall I be industrious and gather berries? Or shall I take an idle stroll?"

Pandora could not make up her mind, for she was thinking of only one thing. As she looked around, trying to decide what to do, she suddenly found herself before the enticing box. For a full minute she stood there, silently wrestling with the impulse to defy Mercury and peek inside.

Slowly Pandora took two steps—then two more. She extended a finger and timidly touched the lid.

"How dusty the box is!" she exclaimed. She took out her handkerchief and began to wipe off the dust that dimmed the luster. As she did so, she put her ear close to the box. A faint noise came from it—a queer humming, buzzing sound.

"There's something alive inside!" she thought. "I wonder what it is! It certainly would not matter if I took just one glimpse. I need open the box scarcely a hair's-breadth."

She put her finger under the edge of the lid and raised it ever so slightly. Then with a gesture of defiance, she lifted the cover. Instantly she was more frightened and regretful than she could have imagined. Before the terrified Pandora could slam the lid shut, a horde of tiny, ugly creatures

came rushing out. They swirled, buzzed, and swarmed hither and thither, uttering spiteful cries. Pandora was frantic and began to weep.

Just as those dreadful little creatures flew out the window, Epimetheus entered the room. At the sight of the open box, he dashed to close it. "Pandora! What have you done?" he shouted in horror.

"I'll tell you what mischief she has done," called a voice.

Pandora and Epimetheus looked up and saw a ray of bright light. Gliding down it into the room was the tall figure of the messenger god.

"Pandora has loosed all the misfortunes, diseases, and sorrows that were shut up in that box," said Mercury. "Now all mankind will be inflicted with these plagues forever."

"Oh, oh!" sobbed the woebegone Pandora.

The god smiled slowly. "Listen!" he said.

They were silent for a moment; then from the box came a tinkling cry. "Let me out!"

"Open the box again," said Mercury.

Epimetheus lifted the lid. There, clinging to the edge of the box, was a lovely fairy creature. On glistening wings she soared up into the room. She touched Epimetheus and Pandora with her finger-tips as she passed, and the room was filled with a comforting glow.

"Who is she?" asked Pandora, who was entranced by the graceful fairy.

"She is Hope," answered Mercury. "She was put in the box to reduce the pain caused by all the creatures of disaster. Mankind will have no need to despair while Hope is in the world."

With that, Mercury vanished on a slanting sunbeam. But Hope remained. As Epimetheus and Pandora looked at the serene creature, they began to smile happily.

Ali Cogia and the Olives

There once lived in Bagdad a very rich merchant
named Ali Cogia. Having neither wife nor child to
care for, he packed his camel for a long journey.
He had sold his household belongings and the wares
from his shop. The only matter that he could not
settle satisfactorily was what to do with his thousand pieces of gold, which he wished to leave behind.

After some thought Ali Cogia hit upon a plan.
He took a large vase and placed the money in it.
Then he covered the gold pieces with olives. After
corking the vase tightly, he carried it to one of
his friends, a merchant like himself.

"My brother," Ali Cogia said, "you have probably heard that I am starting on a long journey. I

have come to ask you to do me a favor. Will you keep this vase of olives for me till I come back?"

His friend agreed and said, "Take this key to my shop and put your vase with my wine jugs. I promise that you shall find it in the same place on your return." Satisfied that his gold was safe, Ali mounted his camel and began his journey.

So it came to pass that seven years slipped by. During all that time the friend with whom Ali had left the vase of olives never once thought about it. Then one day the man's wife remarked that she would like some olives to eat.

"That reminds me," said her husband. "Before Ali Cogia went away, he left a vase of olives in my care. By this time he must be dead. There is no reason why we should not eat the olives if we like."

"Dear husband," begged the wife, "pay no attention to my idle wishes. I really have no desire for olives. Probably, after all this time, they are no longer good. Ali Cogia may yet return. What will he think of you if he should find that the jar has been opened? Do not open it, I entreat you."

The merchant, however, spurned her advice. He took a dish and went out to his shop. When he opened the vase, he found that the topmost olives were rotten. To see if the other olives were in better condition, he shook some out into the dish. As they fell out, a few gold pieces fell out, too.

The sight of the money roused the merchant's greed. Peering down into the vase, he saw that the whole lower part was filled with pieces of gold. Hastily he replaced the old, rotten olives and returned to his wife.

"You are quite right," he told her. "The olives are shriveled. I recorked the vase so well that Ali Cogia will never know it has been touched."

But all that night the merchant wondered how he could manage to keep the gold if his friend should come back and claim the vase. Early the next day he went out and bought some fresh olives. After throwing away the old ones, he took out the gold, hid it, and filled the vase with the new olives he had bought. This done, he recorked the vase and put it back in the place where Ali had left it.

A month later Ali Cogia returned to Bagdad and went to see his friend, the merchant. "I beg you," said Ali, "to return the vase which you have cared for all these seven years."

"Certainly," said the merchant. "I am glad that I could be of service to you. Here is the key to my shop. You will find the vase right where you put it seven years ago."

Ali Cogia fetched his vase, carried it home, and opened it. Eagerly he thrust his hand down into the vase, but he could feel no coins. Then he spilled out the olives. The gold was not there!

In great haste he went back to the shop of the merchant. "My friend," said Ali Cogia, "I can find nowhere in this vase the thousand pieces of gold that I placed underneath the olives."

"Ali," said the merchant, "are you accusing me of stealing? You placed your vase of olives in my charge. You brought it here yourself. You removed it yourself. Now you tell me that it contained a thousand pieces of gold! Did you ever say anything about gold before? If you placed any gold in the vase, it is there still."

Angrily Ali Cogia took the merchant by the arm. "Let us see if you dare repeat your story before the cadi who judges the people of Bagdad."

"I should like nothing better," said the merchant. "We shall see which of us is in the right."

So the two men presented themselves before the cadi. Ali Cogia repeated his tale. His friend stuck to his former statement and offered to swear that he had no knowledge of the thousand pieces of gold in the vase.

"Very well," said the cadi to the merchant. "You were not seen stealing the gold pieces. Therefore, I pronounce you innocent of any crime."

Judgment being given, the merchant went home triumphant. But Ali Cogia decided to draw up a petition requesting a new hearing before the wise and mighty caliph of the land. The next morning Ali presented his petition and was told that the caliph would listen to his case on the morrow.

That evening the caliph went for a walk with his grand vizir. Both were disguised in long, simple robes so that no one would recognize them. While the caliph was strolling along, his attention was attracted by noisy talk. Through a doorway he saw ten or twelve children playing in the moonlight. He hid himself in a dark corner to watch them.

"Let us play at being judge," said one boy. "I will be the cadi. Bring before me Ali Cogia and the merchant who is accused of robbing him of a thousand pieces of gold."

The boy's words made the caliph remember Ali's petition, which he had just received. He waited with interest to see what would happen.

The young cadi took his seat, and the other two children introduced themselves as the merchant and Ali Cogia. The one who was Ali Cogia made a low bow and pleaded his case. Then it was the boy merchant's turn to defend himself. He repeated the story that the real merchant had told.

"Stop a moment," said the make-believe cadi. "I should like to examine the vase with the olives. Ali Cogia, have you the vase with you?" Learning that it was not there, the boy cadi ordered, "Go and get the vase. Bring it to me."

The boy acting the part of Ali Cogia scampered away. Returning quickly, he pretended to set a vase at the feet of the judge. Ali made a movement as if he were uncorking the vase, and the young cadi acted as if he were peering inside.

"What lovely olives!" he said. "I should like to taste one." He pretended to put one in his mouth and said, "They are really excellent. But it seems very odd that olives seven years old should be as juicy as these! Send for two dealers in olives and let us hear what they say."

Two boys were presented to him as olive dealers, and the judge addressed them. "Tell me," he said, "how long can olives be kept and still be pleasant eating?"

"My lord," answered a boy merchant, "no matter how well olives are preserved, they cannot last beyond the third year. They then lose both color and flavor and are only fit to be thrown away."

"If that is so," answered the cadi, "examine this vase and tell me how long these olives have been in it."

The young olive dealers pretended to examine and taste the olives. Then they reported to the judge that the fruit was fresh and good.

"You are mistaken," said the judge. "Ali Cogia swears he put them in the vase seven years ago!"

"My lord," replied the two olive merchants, "we assure you that the olives are those of this year."

The boy playing the part of the rascally merchant protested his innocence; but the cadi said, "You are a thief. You must be punished."

The real caliph was lost in astonishment at the wisdom of the young cadi. "I can perceive no better way to judge the real case," he thought.

Turning to the grand vizir, the caliph spoke. "Tomorrow bring me the young cadi so that the actual case may be tried in his presence. You also must summon the real cadi who pronounced the first judgment on the merchant. Have the real Ali Cogia bring his vase of olives and make sure that two expert olive dealers are in attendance."

So saying, the caliph returned to his palace.

The next day the caliph sat on his throne, with the young boy at his elbow. When Ali Cogia and the merchant appeared, the ruler said, "Now speak, and this child will give you justice."

Ali Cogia and the merchant presented the case. But when the merchant started to swear to his ignorance concerning the gold, he was stopped.

"First let us see the vase of olives," said the youthful judge.

At these words Ali Cogia presented his vase and uncorked it. The caliph took one of the olives, tasted it, and bade the expert olive dealers do the same. They pronounced the olives fresh that very year.

The youth informed the experts that Ali Cogia declared it was seven years since he had placed the fruit in the vase.

The experts replied, "But that is impossible!"

By this time the accused merchant realized that he was certain to be condemned. Quickly he tried to offer an explanation for retaining the gold. But the boy judge said, "Stop! You are a thief."

Then he spoke to the caliph. "Commander of the Faithful, this is not a game. It is not for me to condemn this man. Your Highness must pronounce judgment."

The caliph, convinced that the merchant was a thief, ordered that he be imprisoned. Then the man confessed his guilt and revealed the place in which he had hidden Ali Cogia's gold.

Turning to the real cadi, the caliph sternly advised, "I trust you have listened well enough to learn from the mouth of a child how to deal out true justice."

To the boy the caliph presented one hundred gold coins as a mark of his favor, and then sent him home.

The Winged Horse

Minerva was the gray-eyed goddess who watched over heroes and gave wisdom and skill to those who sincerely wished for these gifts.

Now it happened that Minerva had caught and tamed a wonderful winged horse called Pegasus. Once the horse was tamed, the goddess did not care to ride him herself. She wanted to give him to a mortal who truly deserved to own such a magnificent animal. But until she could find a youth brave enough and wise enough to ride her spirited steed, she gave Pegasus into the care of her nymphs.

273

One day in the city of Corinth there was born a prince named Bellerophon. His father, Glaucus, possessed more skill in handling horses than any man who had ever lived. As soon as Bellerophon was old enough, his father began instructing him in the art of handling spirited horses. Thus it was that while Bellerophon was still extremely young, he knew all the ways of horses and had learned to ride them well.

When Bellerophon was sixteen, he began to wish for travel and adventure. He therefore planned to visit other lands and neighboring kings.

Many friends came to bid farewell to the gallant young man and wish him good fortune. But one came who only pretended to be a friend. He was named Proetus, and he hoped that the young prince would never return from the long journey.

It happened that the jealous Proetus was the son-in-law of Iobates, king of Lycia. Pretending friendship, Proetus gave Bellerophon a letter to carry to the king. The letter demanded that the prince be put to death when he arrived in Lycia. Bellerophon, of course, did not know this. He put the letter under the belt of his tunic and rode off to unknown adventures.

At long last Bellerophon reached Lycia, where Iobates reigned. The young prince found the people oppressed by great sorrow and in constant mourning. Each night a monster called the chimera came down into the valley from its mountain lair and carried off sheep, oxen, women, and children.

Bellerophon rode through the mournful city and came to the palace of Iobates. He presented himself to the monarch and gave him the letter.

As the king read, his face darkened with troubled thoughts. He did not like the request of Proetus. Yet he did not wish to displease his son-in-law. Iobates knew that to put a guest to death would be a wicked deed. He was afraid that such an action would bring war on him from Bellerophon's homeland. So he decided to solve his problem by sending the prince out to slay the chimera. The king was certain that Bellerophon could never come back alive from such a mission.

When King Iobates asked Bellerophon to kill the chimera, the prince was not at all fearful. His love of perilous adventure filled his heart with a great yearning to overcome this evil monster. He was glad to have the chance to free the kingdom from its terrible fear and thus allow the people to cease their mourning.

But Bellerophon was not so rash as to start out in haste. Instead he asked advice of the wisest and oldest man in the kingdom. The aged man was flattered that the prince was humble enough to seek help from someone older. Therefore, he disclosed a secret known to no one else in all the realm. "There is a winged horse that could help you succeed in your mission," he told the prince. "Once I saw this marvelous creature. It was drinking at a well deep in the forest that shelters the temple of Minerva. If you sleep in her temple and offer gifts to the goddess, she may help you find the horse."

Bellerophon found his way to the temple and lay down to sleep. Soon he had a vision of Minerva clad in lustrous silver armor. Her gray eyes shone as though they held sparks of fire. Plumes of blue and rose floated from her helmet. In her hand she carried a golden bridle. "This," she said, "will help you capture the great steed you seek." Then she directed Bellerophon to the well where Pegasus came each night to drink.

When the prince awoke, he saw a golden bridle lying on the floor beside him. With the bridle over his arm, he made his way to the well. There he hid himself among the tall reeds to watch for the coming of the winged horse. At last, far up in the sky, he saw the beautiful flying steed.

Nearer and nearer it came. Then slowly it floated down to the earth. Its silver feet landed softly on the grass beside the well. As the creature bent its head to drink, Bellerophon sprang from his hiding place and caught the horse by its mane. Before Pegasus could free himself, the golden bridle was slipped over his head and the prince was upon his back.

At once Pegasus ascended high into the air, darting wildly through the sky. He reared and plunged, trying to rid himself of his rider. Now he flew among the clouds; now he dived toward the earth.

Bellerophon understood how to handle such fierce horses. He remembered the things his father had taught him and put them to use.

At last Pegasus realized that he had found his master. Tired and panting, the horse dropped to earth beside the well. There the prince had left a sword and a long spear.

After Bellerophon had rested his steed, he armed himself with the weapons. Then he rode toward the chimera's lair. While still high in the air, he sighted the beast on a ledge outside a great cavern. The fierce monster partly resembled a lion and partly a dragon. It lay basking in the sunlight with its great lion's head between its feet. Its long, green, scaly tail—like that of a dragon—was curled around its body.

Bellerophon rode his winged steed as near as he dared to the ledge on which the chimera lay. Raising his spear, he aimed it at the evil brute. Just then it began to belch forth clouds of smoke and fire, causing Pegasus to rear back in sudden terror.

While the beast was drawing in its breath for another flaming puff, Bellerophon approached even closer to the ledge. Then before the chimera could exhale more deadly fire, the prince gave one thrust, sending his long spear right through the heart of the monstrous creature. With one slash of his sword the young man cut off the chimera's head and started back to the palace of Iobates.

The appearance of the prince approaching the castle on his wonderful horse and carrying the head of the evil beast caused wild rejoicing in the city. Everyone praised Bellerophon, and all expressed amazement at the silver feet and magnificent wings of Pegasus.

The young daughter of the king saw the prince and fell in love with him at once. She implored her father to welcome Prince Bellerophon into the royal palace.

King Iobates then decided that he would never carry out the evil request of his son-in-law. Instead, he led the princess to Bellerophon and gave her to him for his bride. From the day of their wedding to the end of their lives, the prince lived happily with his wife in the kingdom of Iobates.

Pegasus, the magnificent winged horse, remained with his master until Bellerophon had no more need of him. Then the goddess Minerva took the great steed back to her home with the gods.

The Lion and the Mouse

A lion with the heat oppress'd,
One day composed himself to rest;
But whilst he dozed, as he intended,
A mouse his royal back ascended;
Nor thought of harm, as Aesop tells,
Mistaking him for some one else;
And travell'd over him, and round him,
And might have left him as she found him
Had she not—tremble when you hear—
Tried to explore the monarch's ear!
Who straightway woke, with wrath immense,
And shook his head to cast her thence.
"You rascal, what are you about?"
Said he, when he had turned her out.
"I'll teach you soon," the lion said,
"To make a mouse-hole in my head!"
So saying, he prepared his foot
To crush the trembling tiny brute;
But she (the mouse) with tearful eye,
Implored the lion's clemency,
Who thought it best at last to give
His little pris'ner a reprieve.

'Twas nearly twelve months after this,
The lion chanced his way to miss;
When pressing forward, heedless yet,
He got entangled in a net.
With dreadful rage, he stampt and tore,
And straight commenced a lordly roar;
When the poor mouse, who heard the noise,
Attended, for she knew his voice.
Then what the lion's utmost strength
Could not effect, she did at length;
With patient labor she applied
Her teeth, the network to divide;
And so at last forth issued he,
A *lion*, by a mouse set free.

Few are so small or weak, I guess,
But may assist us in distress,
Nor shall we ever, if we're wise,
The meanest, or the least despise.

The Adventures of Magboloto

Once in the times when gods and goddesses came down to visit the earth, there was a mortal by the name of Magboloto. He was out hunting one day and by chance entered a secluded glade. Three lovely goddesses were playfully wading in a clear, gurgling brook. Magboloto noticed that they had removed their wings and had placed them on the bank. Silently he crept near and managed to take a pair of the wings without being seen.

When the three goddesses ended their play, they looked for their wings. The pair belonging to Macaya, the youngest goddess, could not be found. Without her wings poor Macaya could not return to the home of the gods. She began to wring her hands and weep when her two companions flew away and left her.

Magboloto, who had hidden the wings, walked over to the lovely Macaya and asked, "Why are you weeping?"

"Why do you ask?" Macaya tearfully inquired.

"Perhaps if you tell me your troubles, I can be of assistance to you," Magboloto replied.

"I have lost my wings and cannot return to my home in the sky," said Macaya, continuing to cry.

"Wings are not used by earthly mortals; so I do not know where to find any," Magboloto told her. "But I shall be only too glad to give you a home if you will marry me."

Since the mortal seemed good and kind, Macaya accepted his offer.

When Magboloto and Macaya had been married a year, a child was born to them. Now it happened that one day Magboloto was making the rice soup for their meal, and Macaya was outside swinging her child in a hammock. All at once the goddess saw that one of the pillars supporting the house had loosened. Sticking out of the hollow bamboo post was something white. Macaya stepped closer to investigate. To her great astonishment and joy she discovered two folded wings—the same pair that she had lost.

Without a moment's hesitation she put on the wings and flew up to the home of the gods, leaving her child and her husband behind.

Magboloto called and called to his wife. When she failed to answer his calls, he became very much alarmed. Then suspecting what had happened, he looked in the bamboo post and saw that the wings were gone. He knew that Macaya had flown back to her home in the sky.

Magboloto loved his goddess wife dearly and was so disconsolate because of her absence that he determined to find her. Leaving the child with his relatives, he set out to seek the home of the gods.

He walked and he walked, all the while choking with great sobs. At last he met North Wind.

"Magboloto, Magboloto, why do you weep?" North Wind asked.

"Ask me nothing if you cannot help me," Magboloto replied.

"Tell me your troubles, and I will help you."

"My wife is a goddess, and she has flown away to return to the dwelling place of the gods. I cannot live without her. Could you show me the way to the home of the gods?"

North Wind said, "I do not know the way. But perhaps my brother East Wind can tell you."

The man searched till he found East Wind.

"Magboloto, Magboloto, why do you weep?" asked the wind.

"Ask me nothing if you cannot help me," the woeful Magboloto replied.

"Tell me your troubles, and I will surely help you," promised East Wind.

Magboloto then confided his melancholy story.

"I do not know the way to the home of the gods," East Wind said. "Perchance my brother South Wind can tell you."

When Magboloto at last found South Wind, he was asked the same question, "Why do you weep?"

"Ask me nothing if you cannot help me," was Magboloto's answer.

"Tell me your troubles," South Wind replied. "I shall try to help you."

So the sad story was told to South Wind.

Regretfully South Wind said, "I cannot tell you how to reach your wife's home. But I feel certain that my brother West Wind can tell you."

Once more the sobbing Magboloto started off on a long search. By and by he met West Wind, who asked, "Why do you weep, Magboloto?"

"Ask me nothing if you cannot help me."

"If you tell me your troubles, I will help you," West Wind promised.

When the story of how Macaya had flown away was told, West Wind said, "I do not know the way to the home of the gods, but King Eagle does."

Magboloto searched a long, long time for the eagle. When he finally saw the regal bird flying in the sky, he called to it. "My goddess wife has left me and my child. Can you tell me how to reach the home of the gods?"

"Not only that," replied the eagle. "I will carry you there on my back."

Magboloto thought that his troubles were over when he reached the home of the gods. But instead of being greeted by his wife, he was met by her ancient grandmother.

Magboloto begged the grandmother to give the goddess permission to return to earth with him.

"I shall give my consent only on one condition," announced the old woman. "First you must scatter ten jars of new millet seed out on the sands to dry. If in the afternoon you can gather up every grain, you may take Macaya to earth."

Eager to perform the task the grandmother had set for him, Magboloto began it at once. He spread ten jars of the exceedingly fine millet seed upon the sands. When the sun was just overhead, he began to gather up the grain and replace it in the jars. But though he worked hard and constantly, he had by sunset been able to replace only a few handfuls. Knowing that it was impossible to complete this irksome task, Magboloto began to sob.

"Magboloto, Magboloto, why do you weep?" asked a tiny voice.

Looking down, the man saw that it was the king of ants who had spoken.

"Ask me nothing if you cannot help me," the sobbing man replied.

"Tell me your troubles, and perhaps I can help you," suggested the king of ants.

Whereupon, Magboloto related his pitiful tale. He told of his wife, who had flown from him, of his intolerable grief for her, and of his long journey in search of her. Lastly he described the impossible task imposed upon him by her grandmother.

"If only I could have gathered up all this grain, I might now have my dear wife by my side," the poor man cried.

"I will help," promised the king of ants. Then he took up a tiny horn and blew upon it.

Immediately a vast army of ants arrived and began gathering up the countless grains. Soon they had all been put back into the jars.

Magboloto thanked the ants politely and took the ten jars to the grandmother.

"Now I will take Macaya to earth," he said.

"No," came the grandmother's withering denial. "Not until you have hulled one hundred bushels of rice. And this must be done by morning."

Magboloto knew that this, too, was a hopeless task. Sitting down beside the great piles of rice, he started to shed bitter tears.

"Magboloto, Magboloto, why do you weep?" asked a squeaky voice nearby.

It was the king of rats speaking.

Looking down through his tears, Magboloto said, "Ask me nothing if you cannot help me."

"I will help you if I can," said the king of rats.

Once again Magboloto told his story. When he had finished, the king of rats brought forth a tiny  flute and blew several shrill notes upon it. Instantly he was surrounded by a large army of rats. They stood stiffly at attention, awaiting their king's command.

"Hull the rice!" the king ordered.

Immediately all the rats began to gnaw the hulls from the rice. In no time at all every grain of rice was as clean as could be.

After thanking the rats, Magboloto hurried away. Early the next morning he appeared before the old grandmother with the rice. He demanded that she give his wife into his keeping.

"No!" said the grandmother. "Not till you've chopped down every tree on yonder mountain!"

Now Magboloto knew that this task was utterly impossible. He could not restrain his tears.

"Magboloto, Magboloto, why do you weep?" asked a voice.

Still sobbing, Magboloto saw that it was the king of boars who had addressed him.

"Ask me nothing if you cannot help me."

"Perhaps I can help you," said the king of boars.

So Magboloto repeated all that had happened.

"I will do what I can for you," promised the king of boars.

He took a horn and blew several sharp blasts upon it. At once he was surrounded by a herd of savage-looking boars.

"Cut down the trees on yonder mountain!" the king commanded.

In a little while the wild boars had felled all the trees with their sharp tusks. Magboloto was exceedingly thankful and said so.

Now when Macaya's old grandmother saw that Magboloto had been able to perform every difficult task she had given him, she believed that he was the right husband for the goddess. Consequently, she gave them her blessing.

Magboloto was overjoyed to have his wife with him again. Macaya, too, was glad to return to her family. She and Magboloto and their children lived together happily upon the earth until the end of their days.

Magnificat of the Heart

There were once three aged men who, desiring to serve God in solitude, withdrew to the wilderness. They built themselves a small hermitage and a chapel, and passed their days in peace and contentment. Their chief joy was to meet daily in the chapel for the worship of God.

True, the hermits had one deep regret. Since they were old and feeble, they could not offer praise to God in musical fashion. For one of them croaked like a raven, another was hoarse like a crow, and the third had a voice so weak that he could scarcely raise it above a whisper.

Thus the three old men had to be content with merely reciting the offices of the Church and the hymns and Psalms. They trusted that the merciful God, knowing they could do no better, would graciously accept what they offered Him with all their hearts.

It seemed to them especially sad that Our Lady's hymn, the Magnificat, should ascend to Heaven spoken in such a manner. Every evening, therefore, after Vespers had been said and it was time for the Magnificat, the three hermits uplifted their poor voices and sang reverently that hymn to the glory of God and Our Lady. Knowing they had given their best, they were content.

One day there came to the hermitage a young man
of gentle bearing. He was a minstrel who said he
had grown weary of living among men. He asked
permission to remain with the hermits in the wilderness, serving God and Our Lady.

After taking counsel together, the three old men
agreed to his request and made him welcome.

That same evening, when the hermits went to the
chapel for Vespers, the young stranger took his
place among them. When it was time to sing the
Magnificat, he lifted up his voice proudly and sang
like a lark. So very melodious was the sound that

the three old men listened in rapture, amazed and overjoyed, and entirely forgot to sing themselves.

Silently they rejoiced that henceforth in their humble chapel the Magnificat would be sung in a fashion that would do honor to God and Our Lady.

When the young man had finished singing, he retired. His three companions remained in the chapel to thank God for the great good fortune that had come to them, when lo, an angel of the Lord came down and stood by the altar.

"I come," said the angel, "sent by God to ask why no hymn ascended to Him tonight from this place. The Magnificat He has not heard."

The old men looked at one another in surprise. Then as the angel vanished, they began to understand the meaning of his gentle rebuke.

In listening to the wonderful singing of the young stranger they had forgotten to lift up their hearts to God in that hymn of praise. And since it is the worship of the heart alone that reaches to the throne of God, no hymn from the chapel had sounded in the courts of Heaven that night.

Going straightway to the stranger, the old men said, "Thou must depart. If not, who can tell whether, listening to thy golden voice, we might not again forget to praise God. Therefore go in peace and serve Him in some other place."

Sorrowfully the young man departed. Once again the hermits lived alone.

Each evening they sang the Magnificat reverently, as they had done before the stranger appeared. One of them croaked like a raven, another was hoarse like a crow, and the third had a voice so weak that he could scarcely raise it above a whisper. But all three were heard in Heaven. For although their voices were not melodious, their hearts sang loud to the honor and glory of God. And to the song of their hearts did He give ear.

BOOKS TO READ

Here are some good books that provide more of the same fun and adventure we find in *More People and Progress*.

World Neighbors

Call It Courage. Armstrong Sperry.
Dobry. Monica Shannon.
Hans Brinker or The Silver Skates. Mary Mapes Dodge.
Heritage. Hilda K. F. Gull.
Kaatje and the Christmas Compass. Alta H. Seymour.
Little Boat Boy. A Story of Kashmir. Jean Bothwell.
My Village in Ireland. Tim and Sonia Gidal.
Pedro's Coconut Skates. Esther Wood.
The Adventures of Kenji of Japan. Albert J. Nevins.
The Cottage at Bantry Bay. Hilda van Stockum.
The Good Master. Kate Seredy.
The Wheel on the School. Meindert De Jong.

The World of Nature

Bubo, the Great Horned Owl. John and Jean George.
Burma Boy. Willis Lindquist and Nicolas Mordvinoff.
Kalak of the Ice. Jim Kjelgaard.
Marlin Perkins' Zooparade. Marlin Perkins.
Old Con and Patrick. Ruth Sawyer.
Paddlewings: Penguin of Galapagos. Wilfrid Bronson.
The Caves of the Great Hunters. Hans Baumann.
The Mystery of Mont Saint-Michel. Michael Rouzé.
Zoo Babies. William Bridges.
Zoo Expeditions. William Bridges.

Men of Progress

City Neighbor: The Story of Jane Addams. Clara Ingram Judson.
Henry Ford, Engineer. Louise A. Neyhart.

John Wanamaker: Boy Merchant. Olive W. Burt.
Marconi: Pioneer of Radio. Douglas Coe.
Modern Crusaders. John Travers Moore and Rosemarian V. Staudacher.
Mr. Bell Invents the Telephone. Katherine Shippen.
My Eskimos: A Priest in the Arctic. Roger Buliard, O.M.I.
Nickels and Dimes. Nina Baker.
The Story of Amelia Earhart. Adèle De Leeuw.

In the Shadow of the Cathedrals

From Star to Star. Eric P. Kelly.
Imps and Angels. Jane Gilbert.
Little Dusty Foot. Marian W. Magoon.
Medieval Days and Ways. Gertrude Hartman.
Saint Philip of the Joyous Heart. Francis X. Connolly.
Simon o' the Stock. Anne Heagney.
The Book of Ralf. Phillis Garrard.
The Boy Knight of Reims. Eloise Lownsbery.
The Crusade and the Cup. Elizabeth Bleecker Meigs.
The Door in the Wall. Marguerite de Angeli.
The Hidden Treasure of Glaston. Eleanore M. Jewett.
The Lost Dragon of Wessex. Gwendolyn Bowers.
The Sword in the Tree. Clyde Robert Bulla.

Tales from Many Lands

Adventures with the Giants. Catherine F. Sellew.
Aesop's Fables. George T. Townsend and Thomas James.
Arabian Nights. Andrew Lang.
Children of Odin. Padraic Colum.
In the Morning of the World. Janette S. Lowrey.
Once the Hodja. Alice Geer Kelsey.
Once the Mullah. Alice Geer Kelsey.
Tales of Faraway Folk. Babette Deutsch and Avrahm Yarmolinsky.
The Priceless Cats and Other Italian Folk Stories. M. A. Jagendorf.

Full Pronunciation Key

The pronunciation of each word is shown just after the word, in this way: **ab bre vi ate** (ə brē′vi āt). The letters and signs used are pronounced as in the words below. The mark ′ is placed after a syllable with primary or heavy accent, as in the example above. The mark ′ after a syllable shows a secondary or lighter accent, as in **ab bre vi a tion** (ə brē′vi ā′shən).

a	hat, cap	j	jam, enjoy	u	cup, butter
ā	age, face	k	kind, seek	u̇	full, put
ã	care, air	l	land, coal	ü	rule, move
ä	father, far	m	me, am	ū	use, music
		n	no, in		
b	bad, rob	ng	long, bring		
ch	child, much			v	very, save
d	did, red	o	hot, rock	w	will, woman
		ō	open, go	y	young, yet
e	let, best	ô	order, all	z	zero, breeze
ē	equal, be	oi	oil, voice	zh	measure, seizure
ėr	term, learn	ou	house, out		
				ə	represents:
f	fat, if	p	paper, cup		a in about
g	go, bag	r	run, try		e in taken
h	he, how	s	say, yes		i in pencil
		sh	she, rush		o in lemon
i	it, pin	t	tell, it		u in circus
ī	ice, five	th	thin, both		
		ŦH	then, smooth		

This pronunciation key is from the *Thorndike-Barnhart Junior Dictionary*. Special acknowledgment is made to Clarence L. Barnhart, editor of the Thorndike-Barnhart Dictionaries, for his assistance in the preparation of this glossary.

ab bot (ab′ət), man who is the head of a group of monks dwelling together and living a religious life.

a cad e my (ə kad′ə mi), 1. a place for instruction. 2. school where some special subject can be studied. There are academies of medicine and painting, and military or naval academies.

Academy Bay, bay on the coast of Indefatigable Island.

ac claim (ə klām′), 1. applaud; shout welcome; show approval of. 2. announce with signs of approval; hail. 3. applause; welcome.

ac com mo da tion (ə kom′ə dā′-shən), 1. room; lodging for a time: *This hotel has accommodations for one hundred people.* 2. a help; a convenience: *It will be an accommodation to me if you will meet me tomorrow instead of today.*

ad mi ral (ad′mə rəl), 1. officer in command of a fleet of ships. 2. officer of the highest rank in the navy.

ad mon ish (ad mon′ish), warn or advise (a person) about his faults in order that he may be guided to improve: *The policeman admonished him not to drive too fast.*

aer i al (ār′i əl), 1. of the air; in the air; consisting of air. 2. a device with a radio set to receive the electric waves. 3. the wire or wires used in sending by radio.

ag gres sive (ə gres′iv), 1. taking the first step in an attack or quarrel; attacking. 2. active; energetic.

ag ile (aj′əl), moving quickly and easily; active; lively; nimble: *An acrobat has to be agile. You need an agile mind to solve puzzles.*

ag ri cul tur al (ag′rə kul′chər əl), of agriculture; having to do with farming.

ag ri cul ture (ag′rə kul′chər), farming; cultivating the soil to make crops grow.

A lain (ä lan′ or a′lən).

al che mist (al′kə mist), man who studied chemistry and magic in the Middle Ages. The alchemists tried to turn lead into gold.

A li (ä′li).

am e thyst (am′ə thist), a purple or violet quartz used for jewelry.

A ni ta (ä nē′tä).

An ne tje (än′ā chə).

an tics (an′tiks), funny gestures and actions; silly tricks; capers: *The clown amused us by his antics.*

a ris to crat (ə ris′tə krat), 1. person who belongs to the ruling class; a noble. 2. person who has the tastes, opinions, manners, etc., of the upper class.

As gard (as′gärd or az′gärd), the home of the Norse gods and heroes.

at tain (ə tān′), 1. arrive at; reach. 2. gain; accomplish.

at tend (ə tend′), 1. be present at: *Children must attend school.* 2. give care and thought; apply oneself: *Attend to your lessons.*

at tend ance (ə ten′dəns), 1. attending: *Our class has perfect attendance today.* 2. company present; persons attending: *The attendance at church was over 200 last Sunday.*

at tract (ə trakt′), 1. draw to oneself: *The magnet attracted the iron.* 2. be pleasing to; win the attention and liking of: *Bright colors attract children.*

at trac tive (ə trak′tiv), 1. pleasing; winning attention and liking. 2. attracting.

Aus tral ia (ôs trāl′yə), a continent southeast of Asia.

Aus tral ian (ôs trāl′yən), 1. of Australia or its people. 2. a native or inhabitant of Australia.

av a lanche (av′ə lanch), 1. a large mass of snow and ice, or of dirt and rocks, sliding or falling down the side of a mountain. 2. anything like an avalanche: *an avalanche of questions.*

Ave atque vale

A ve at que va le (ä′vä ät′kwä
vä′lā), Hail and farewell! *Phrase pop-
ular among Latin students. It comes
from a poem by Catullus, who lived in
Rome before Christ was born. The poem
is a sad good-by to the poet's brother,
who died when very young.*

bade (bad). See **bid.**
Bang kok (bang′kok),   capital and
chief port of Thailand (Siam).
Ba reil ly (bə rā′li).
bar ri o (bär′ē ō),   a subdivision of
a municipality. A barrio is usually a
village or settlement.
Bas ra (bus′rə or bas′rə),   seaport
in Iraq, near the Persian Gulf.
ba zaar   or   **ba zar**   (bə zär′),
1. street or streets full of shops in
Oriental countries. **2.** place for the
sale of many kinds of goods. **3.** sale
held for some special purpose.
be deck (bi dek′),   adorn.
be drag gled (bi drag′əld),   **1.** wet
and hanging limp. **2.** dragged in the
dirt.
Bei rut (bā rüt′),   capital of Lebanon.
Be jaun us (bā jon′əs or bə jôn′əs),
1. baby bird; a nestling. **2.** inexperienced person, especially a beginning
student. *Used in common talk long ago.*
be la bor (bi lā′bər),   **1.** beat vigor-
ously; **2.** abuse; belittle.
Bel ler o phon (bə ler′ə fon),   in
Greek legend, a hero who killed a
dreadful monster with the help of
the winged horse Pegasus.
bel lig er ent (bə lij′ər ənt),   **1.** at
war; engaged in war. **2.** a nation or
a person engaged in war. **3.** warlike;
quarrelsome.
Ber tin (ber′tan).
be siege (bi sēj′),   **1.** make a long-
continued attempt to get possession
of (a place) by armed force; sur-
round and try to capture. **2.** crowd
around: *Hundreds of admirers be-*

cadi

sieged the famous aviator. **3.** over-
whelm with requests, questions, etc.:
*During the flood, the Red Cross was
besieged with calls for help.*
bev y (bev′i),   small group: *a bevy
of quail, a bevy of girls.*
bid (bid),   **1.** command: *Do as I bid
you.* **2.** invite: *Our friends gave us
strawberries and bade us come again
in apple time.* **3.** say; tell: *His friends
came to bid him good-by.*
bid ding (bid′ing),   **1.** command.
2. invitation. **3. Do one's bidding**
means to obey one.
Bloe men (blü′mən).
boar (bôr),   **1.** a male pig or hog.
2. a wild pig or hog.
bod ice (bod′is),   close-fitting waist
of a woman's dress.
bois ter ous   (bois′tər əs or bois′-
trəs),   **1.** noisily cheerful: *a boisterous
game.* **2.** violent; rough: *a boisterous
wind, a boisterous child.*
Brit ish (brit′ish),   of Great Britain,
the British Empire, or its people.
British Isles,   Great Britain, Ireland, the Isle of Man, and nearby
islands.
bronze (bronz),   **1.** a brown alloy of
copper with tin. **2.** made of bronze.
3. the color of bronze; yellowish
brown; reddish brown. **4.** make or
become bronze in color: *His skin is
bronzed from the sun.*
brood (brüd),   **1.** the young birds
hatched at one time in the nest, or
cared for together. **2.** young who are
cared for. **3.** sit on. Hens and birds
brood their eggs till the young hatch
out. **4.** think a long time about some
one thing.
bur go mas ter (ber′gə mas′tər),
mayor of a town in the Netherlands,
Flanders, or Germany.

Ca bral (kə bräl′).
ca di (kä′di or kā′di),   a minor
Mohammedan judge.

cal cu late (kal′kū lāt), **1.** reckon; add, subtract, multiply, divide, etc., in order to find out something: *to calculate the cost of furnishing a house.* **2.** find out beforehand by any process of reasoning: *to calculate the day of the week on which Christmas will fall.* **3.** plan; intend: *That remark was calculated to hurt someone's feelings.* **4.** rely; count.

cal cu la tion (kal′kū lā′shən), **1.** adding, subtracting, multiplying, or dividing to find a result. **2.** the result found by calculating. **3.** careful thinking; deliberate planning.

Cal cut ta (kal kut′ə), large city in eastern India.

cal lous (kal′əs), **1.** hard; hardened: *Going barefoot made the bottoms of his feet callous.* **2.** unfeeling: *Only such a callous person as he could see suffering without trying to relieve it.*

car cass (kar′kəs), **1.** dead body of an animal. **2.** body.

ca tas tro phe (kə tas′trə fi), a sudden, widespread, or extraordinary disaster; great calamity or misfortune. A big earthquake is a catastrophe.

Ca thay (ka thā′), old name for China.

ca the dral (kə thē′drəl), the official church of a bishop and mother church of the diocese.

ca vort (kə vôrt′), prance about: *The horses cavorted with excitement.*

chap pat ti (chä pät′i).

Char le magne (shär′lə mān), Charles the Great (742?-814 A.D.), wise and powerful Frankish emperor who brought all the peoples of western Europe together under his rule and gave them a system of laws.

chide (chīd), reprove; express dissatisfaction or displeasure with some-

one; scold; blame: *The nurse chided them for waking the sick baby.*

chi me ra or **chi mae ra** (kə mēr′ə), an imaginary monster with a lion's head, a goat's body, and a serpent's tail. A chimera was supposed to breathe fire.

chim pan zee (chim′pan zē′ or chim pan′zi), an African ape as big as a large dog. Chimpanzees are very intelligent.

chi tal (chē′təl).

chiv al ry (shiv′əl ri), **1.** qualities of an ideal knight. Chivalry includes bravery, honor, courtesy, respect for women, protection of the weak, generosity, and fairness to enemies. **2.** rules and customs of knights in the Middle Ages. **3.** knights as a group.

chor is ter (kôr′is tər), a choirboy; one of a group of singers, especially those taking part in a church service.

chor tle (chôr′təl), chuckle loudly.

clem en cy (klem′ən si), **1.** mercy: *The judge showed clemency to the prisoner.* **2.** mildness: *The clemency of the weather allowed them to live outdoors.*

Co gi a (kō′gi ə).

co her er (kō hēr′ər), device for detecting radio waves, formerly used instead of vacuum tubes in radios.

com mon place (kom′ən plās′), **1.** everyday thing: *The commonplaces of our civilization, from watches to automobiles, are objects of wonder to savages.* **2.** ordinary; not new or interesting.

com mune (kə mūn′), talk in an intimate way.

com mu ni ca tion (kə mū·nə kā′shən), **1.** giving information or news by speaking or writing. **2.** the information·given; letter, message, etc.

---

hat, āge, cãre, fär; let, ēqual, tėrm; it, īce; hot, ōpen, ôrder; oil, out; cup, pút, rüle, ūse; ch, child; ng, long; sh, she; th, thin; ŦH, then; zh, measure; ə represents *a* in about, *e* in taken, *i* in pencil, *o* in lemon, *u* in circus.

com pas sion (kəm pash′ən), a sharing in the feeling of another's sorrow or hardship which leads us to help; sympathy: *The virtue of mercy prompts compassion for those in spiritual or bodily want.*

com plex ion (kəm plek′shən), the color, quality, and general appearance of the skin, particularly of the face.

com pli cate (kom′plə kāt), **1.** mix up; make complex; make hard to understand, settle, cure, etc.: *Too many rules complicate a game.* **2.** make worse or more mixed up: *a headache complicated by eye trouble.*

con demn (kən dem′), **1.** express strong disapproval of: *He condemns cruelty and cruel people.* **2.** pronounce guilty of crime or wrong: *The prisoner is sure to be condemned.* **3.** to doom: *condemned to death.* **4.** declare not sound or suitable for use: *This bridge has been condemned because it is no longer safe.*

con front (kən frunt′), **1.** meet face to face; stand facing. **2.** face boldly; oppose. **3.** bring face to face; place before.

con gress (kong′gris), **1.** coming together; meeting. **2.** a meeting of representatives for the discussion of some subject. **3.** the national law-making body of the United States, composed of the Senate and the House of Representatives, with members elected from every state. The Capitol at Washington is the place where Congress meets.

con se quent ly (kon′sə kwent li), as a result; therefore.

con ser va tion (kon′sər vā′shən), preservation; avoidance of waste: *The conservation of forests is very important.*

con ser va tion ist (kon′sər vā′-shən ist), person who believes in and advocates conservation of the forests, rivers, etc., of a country.

con strict (kən strikt′), draw together; contract; compress: *A rubber band can constrict what it encircles.*

con tor tion (kən tôr′shən), **1.** twisting. **2.** twisted condition: *The acrobat went through various contortions.*

cor du roy (kôr′də roi), thick cloth with close, velvetlike ridges.

Cor inth (kôr′inth), city in ancient Greece which was noted for its art and luxury.

cow lick (kou′lik′), a small tuft of hair that will not lie flat.

cra dle (krā′dəl), **1.** a baby's little bed on rockers. **2.** a frame fastened to a scythe for laying grain evenly as it is cut.

crag (krag), a steep, rugged rock rising above others.

cres cent (kres′ənt), **1.** shape of the moon in its first or last quarter. **2.** anything that curves in a similar way, such as a street or a row of houses. **3.** shaped like the moon in its first or last quarter.

cru sade (krü sād′), **1.** one of the series of wars carried on between 1096 and 1272 by Christians of Europe to recover the Holy Land from Mohammedans. Soldiers of **the Crusades** learned much about life in other countries during their travels. **2.** a vigorous movement against a public evil or in favor of some new idea. **3.** take part in a crusade.

cyl in der (sil′ən dər), **1.** a hollow or solid body shaped like a roller. **2.** any long, round object, solid or hollow, with flat ends. **3.** the piston chamber of an engine.

Cylinder

da is (dā′is), raised platform at the end of a hall or large room.

de fend (di fend′), **1.** guard from attack or harm; protect. **2.** act, speak, or write in favor of.

de fense (di fens´), **1.** defending: *Thanks for your defense of Tim from that bully.* **2.** being defended. **3.** any thing, act, or word that defends, guards, or protects: *A wall around a city was a defense against enemies.*

de fen sive (di fen´siv), **1.** on the defense; defending; ready to defend; intended to defend: *France fought a defensive war.* **2.** defensive position or attitude.

Del hi (del´i),   city in northern India.

de mol ish (di mol´ish),   pull or tear down; destroy.

de stroy (di stroi´),   pull down; break to pieces; spoil; ruin; put an end to; kill.

de struc tion (di struk´shən), **1.** destroying: *A crowd watched the destruction of the old building.* **2.** ruin: *The storm left destruction behind it.*

Dinosaur

di no saur (dī´nə sôr), one of a group of extinct reptiles. Some dinosaurs were bigger than elephants. Some were smaller than cats.

dis con so late   (dis kon´sə lit), without hope; forlorn; unhappy; cheerless: *Mary was disconsolate because her kitten died.*

dis turb (dis tèrb´), **1.** break in upon with noise or change: *Do not disturb the baby; he is asleep.* **2.** make uneasy; trouble: *He was disturbed to hear of her illness.*

dis turb ance (dis tèr´bəns), **1.** a disturbing or being disturbed. **2.** thing that disturbs. **3.** confusion; disorder.

di vert (də vèrt´), **1.** turn aside: *A ditch diverted water from the stream into the fields. The rattle diverted the baby's attention from the knife.* **2.** amuse: *We were diverted by the clown's tricks.*

di vide (də vīd´), **1.** separate into parts. **2.** separate into equal parts: *When you divide 8 by 2, you get 4.* **3.** to share: *The children divided the candy.*

di vi sion (də vizh´ən), **1.** dividing; being divided. **2.** giving some to each; sharing. **3.** the process of dividing one number by another.

dom (dōm),   in Portugal, a title of a gentleman used about the same as our Mr. or sir.

do main (dō mān´),   the lands belonging to a ruler, a nobleman, or a government, and under his or its rule.

dor mi to ry (dôr´mə tô´ri), **1.** a building containing a large number of sleeping rooms. **2.** a sleeping room large enough for a number of beds.

dote (dōt), **1.** be weak-minded and childish because of old age. **2. Dote on** means be foolishly fond of; be fond of.

ed dy (ed´i),   a small whirlpool or whirlwind; water, air, or smoke whirling around.

Ed in burgh (ed´ən bèr´ō),   the capital of Scotland.

ef fi cient (i fish´ənt),   capable; doing things without waste.

em i nence (em´ə nəns), **1.** high position; greatness. **2.** high point of land. **3.** title of a cardinal in the Catholic Church.

en am or (en am´ər),   arouse to love; charm. **Enamored of** means in love with or charmed by.

---

hat, āge, cãre, fär; let, ēqual, tèrm; it, īce; hot, ōpen, ôrder; oil, out; cup, pút, rüle, ūse; ch, child; ng, long; sh, she; th, thin; ᴛн, then; zh, measure; ə represents *a* in about, *e* in taken, *i* in pencil, *o* in lemon, *u* in circus.

en mi ty (en′mə ti), the feeling that enemies have for each other; hate.

en tice (en tīs′), attract; lead into something by raising hopes or desires; tempt: *The smell of food enticed the hungry children into the hut.*

en treat (en trēt′), keep asking earnestly; beg and pray. Also spelled **intreat.**

Ep i me theus (ep′ə mē′thüs).

e ro sion (i rō′zhən), eating away; being worn away: *In geography, we study the erosion of the earth by water.*

es tate (es tāt′), **1.** the total of all goods, land, and money which one person owns. **2.** a large piece of land belonging to a person; landed property. **3.** a class or condition in life: *A boy reaches man's estate at 21.*

es ti ma tion (es′tə mā′shən), opinion; judgment: *In my estimation, your plan will not work.*

ex pect (eks pekt′), look for; think something will come or happen: *We expect hot days in summer.*

ex pect ant (eks pek′tənt), expecting; looking for; thinking something will come or happen: *Mary opened her package with an expectant smile.*

ex qui site (eks′kwi zit), **1.** very lovely; delicate; beautifully made. **2.** sharp: *exquisite pain.* **3.** of highest excellence; most admirable: *She has exquisite taste.*

fad (fad), a fashion or craze; something everybody is doing for a time.

fair (fãr), a courteous title of address: *God save you, fair sir. Old use.*

fair ly (fãr′li), **1.** in a fair manner; without unfair advantage; justly. **2.** moderately; rather. **3.** actually; positively: *She was fairly exhausted with hard work.*

fi es ta (fi es′tə), **1.** religious festival; saint's day. **2.** holiday; festivity.

Fil i pi no (fil′ə pē′nō), a native of the Philippine Islands.

finch (finch), a small songbird. Sparrows, buntings, and canaries are finches.

fis sure (fish′ər), a split; a crack; long, narrow opening.

fledg ling (flej′ling), **1.** a young bird just able to fly. **2.** inexperienced person.

Flor en tine (flôr′ən tēn), **1.** having to do with Florence, a city in Italy. **2.** a native or inhabitant of Florence, Italy.

flu o rite (flü′ə rīt), a transparent, crystalline mineral that occurs in many colors. It is used for fusing metals, making glass, etc.

foal (fōl), newborn horse or donkey.

forge[1] (fôrj), **1.** place with fire where metal is heated very hot and then hammered into shape. A blacksmith uses a forge. **2.** heat (metal) very hot and then hammer into shape: *The blacksmith forged a bar of iron into a big strong hook.* **3.** place where iron or other metal is melted and refined.

Blacksmith's forge

forge[2] (fôrj), move forward slowly but steadily: *One runner forged ahead of the others and won the race.*

Frans (fränts).

fresh et (fresh′it), **1.** a flood caused by heavy rains or melted snow. **2.** a rush of fresh water flowing into the sea.

fry[1] (frī), cook in fat, in a deep or shallow pan.

fry[2] (frī), young fishes.

Ga lá pa gos Islands (gə lä′pə gəs or gə lä′pə gōs), group of islands in the Pacific, 600 miles west of and belonging to Ecuador.

gal ler y (gal′ər i), **1.** a hall or long narrow passage. **2.** a balcony looking down into a large hall or room. **3.** the highest balcony of a theater. **4.** a building or room used to show collections of pictures and statues.

gape (gāp), **1.** open wide: *A deep hole in the earth gaped before us.* **2.** open the mouth wide; yawn. **3.** stare with the mouth open.

Gar cí a (gär sē′ä).

gen er ate (jen′ər āt), produce; cause to be: *Burning coal can generate steam. The steam can generate electricity by turning an electric generator.*

gen er a tor (jen′ər ā′tər), **1.** person or thing that generates. **2.** apparatus for producing electricity, gas, or steam.

gill (gil), a part of the body arranged for breathing in water. Fish and tadpoles have gills.

glade (glād), a little open space in a wood or forest.

Glau cus (glô′kəs).

gorge (gôrj), **1.** a deep, narrow valley, usually steep and rocky. **2.** eat greedily until full.

Gorge

Grail (grāl), the Holy Grail, cup or dish used by Christ at the Last Supper. According to legend, it will be found only if the seeker is a very good and holy person.

grap ple (grap′əl), **1.** seize and hold fast; grip or hold firmly. **2.** struggle; fight. **3.** A **grappling iron** is an iron bar with hooks at one end.

Guam (gwäm), an island in the Pacific Ocean east of the Philippines. Guam belongs to the United States.

guid ance (gīd′əns), guiding; direction; leadership: *Under her mother's guidance, Nell learned how to cook.*

guide (gīd), **1.** show the way; lead; direct. **2.** person or thing that shows the way. **3.** manage; control; regulate.

Gui do (gwē′dō).

guild (gild), society for mutual aid or for some common purpose. In the Middle Ages, a guild was a union of the men in one trade to keep its standards high, and to look out for its interests.

guil der (gil′dər), a Dutch silver coin.

guilds man (gilds mən), member of a guild, particularly medieval guilds.

Ha kim (hä′kim).

haugh ti ly (hô′tə li), in a haughty manner: *Amy tossed her head haughtily.*

haugh ty (hô′ti), **1.** too proud of oneself and too scornful of others: *a haughty girl.* **2.** showing such pride and scorn: *a haughty glance.*

haunt (hônt), **1.** go often to; visit frequently: *People say ghosts haunt that old house.* **2.** place visited often. **3.** be often with: *Memories of his youth haunted the old man.*

Ha wai i (hə wī′ē), **1.** Hawaiian Islands. **2.** the largest of the Hawaiian Islands.

Ha wai ian (hə wī′yən), of or having to do with Hawaii, its people, or their language.

Hawaiian Islands, island group in the North Pacific Ocean, a Territory of the United States.

hat, āge, cãre, fär; let, ēqual, tèrm; it, īce; hot, ōpen, ôrder; oil, out; cup, pùt, rüle, ūse; ch, child; ng, long; sh, she; th, thin; ₮H, then; zh, measure; ə represents *a* in about, *e* in taken, *i* in pencil, *o* in lemon, *u* in circus.

haz ard (haz′ərd), risk; danger: *The life of an aviator is full of hazards.*

heath er (heŦH′ər), a low shrub which covers waste lands in Scotland and northern England.

her mit (hèr′mit), in the Catholic Church, a person who lives away from others in order to draw closer to God.

her mit age (hèr′mə tij), **1.** home of a hermit. **2.** place to live away from others.

Hey nal (hā′näl), Hymn to Our Lady played hourly on a trumpet from Panna Marya church tower in Krakow. Since the Tartar invasion of 1241, it always ends on a broken note in memory of a heroic trumpeter killed by a Tartar arrow which struck him as he played.

home stead (hōm′sted), **1.** a house with its buildings and grounds; a farm with its buildings. **2.** land granted to a settler under certain conditions by the United States government.

Hong Kong or **Hong kong** (hong′ kong′), a seaport city in southeastern China.

Hon o lu lu (hon′ə lü′lü), the capital of the Hawaiian Islands.

hu mil i ate (hū mil′i āt), lower the pride, dignity, or self-respect of: *We felt humiliated by our failure.*

hu mil i a tion (hū mil′i ā′shən), state or feeling of being humiliated.

hu mil i ty (hū mil′ə ti), moral virtue of being honest with ourselves about our shortcomings as well as the abilities God has given us; modesty of spirit; control of pride.

hur ri cane (hèr′ə kān), tropical cyclone; storm with violent wind and, usually, very heavy rain. The wind in a hurricane blows from 70 to 100 miles per hour.

i gua na (i gwä′nə), a large climbing lizard found in tropical countries.

im port (im pôrt′ for 1 and 3, im′- pôrt for 2 and 4), **1.** bring in from a foreign country: *The United States imports sugar from Cuba.* **2.** an article brought into a country. **3.** mean; make known: *What did the King's message import?* **4.** meaning.

in de fat i ga ble (in′di fat′ə gə bəl), never getting tired or giving up; tireless.

Indefatigable Island, one of the four largest of the Galápagos Islands.

in dif fer ent (in dif′ər ənt), **1.** not caring one way or the other. **2.** unimportant; not mattering much. **3.** having or showing no interest.

in sti tu tion (in′stə tü′shən or in′- stə tū′shən), **1.** something established, such as a law, custom, society, club, college, or any organization. **2.** a building used for the work of an institution.

in sur mount a ble (in′sèr moun′- tə bəl), which cannot be overcome.

in tol er a ble (in tol′ər ə bəl), unbearable; too hard to be endured: *The pain from the toothache was intolerable.*

in ven to ry (in′vən tô′ri), **1.** detailed list of articles. **2.** collection of articles that are or may be so listed; stock: *A storekeeper had a sale to reduce his inventory.* **3.** make a detailed list of; enter in a list: *Some stores inventory their stock once a month.*

I o ba tes (ī ō′bə tēz).

I raq (i rak′ or i räk′), a country between Iran and Arabia.

irk some (èrk′səm), tiresome; tedious.

jaunt (jônt), **1.** a short trip; a short pleasure trip or excursion. **2.** take a short pleasure trip.

jet sam (jet′səm), goods which are thrown overboard to lighten a ship in distress and are often washed ashore.

jo ey (jō′i), an Australian word for a young kangaroo.

jour nal (jėr′nəl), **1.** a daily record. **2.** an account of what happens, or of what one thinks, feels, or notices, such as a diary or the written account of what happens at each meeting of a society. **3.** a newspaper or magazine.

joust (just or joust), **1.** a combat between two knights on horseback, armed with lances. **2.** fight with lances on horseback: *Knights used to joust each other for sport.*

Juf frouw (yü′frō), a Dutch word meaning Miss.

Kaa tje (kä′chə).

Ka ra chi (kə rä′chi), capital of Pakistan, in the western part.

Kar el (kä′rəl).

Kees (kās).

kilt (kilt), **1.** pleated skirt, reaching to the knees, worn by men in the Scottish Highlands. **2.** to make pleats in (a garment).

Kim ba (kim′bə).

Man wearing a kilt

knight (nīt), **1.** in the Middle Ages, a man especially trained for a high military rank, and sworn to defend God and the king with honor and virtue. (See **squire**.) **2.** in modern times, a man raised to an honorable rank because of his achievement or service: *Sir Winston Churchill was named a knight of the Order of the Garter in 1953.* **3.** to make a man a knight.

knight hood (nīt′hud), **1.** the rank or dignity of a knight. **2.** the profession or occupation of a knight. **3.** knights: *All the knighthood of France stood ready.*

Koop dam (kō′däm).

Krak ow (krak′ou or krä′kō), city in southern Poland; in the Middle Ages, capital and center of learning.

la va (lä′və), **1.** molten rock flowing from a volcano. **2.** rock formed by the cooling of this molten rock. Some lavas are hard and glassy; others are light and porous.

Leb a non (leb′ə nən), country in southwestern Asia.

leech (lēch), **1.** worm living in ponds and streams that sucks the blood of animals. Doctors once used leeches to suck blood from sick people. **2.** person who tries persistently to get what he can out of others. **3.** in the Middle Ages, a name for doctor, or "one who heals." Since the people knew little about medicine, they were sometimes fooled by dishonest men who pretended to be doctors.

leop ard (lep′ərd), a fierce animal of Africa and Asia, having a dull-yellowish skin spotted with black.

Lex ing ton (lek′sing tən), **1.** a town in eastern Massachusetts where the first battle of the Revolutionary War was fought on April 19, 1775. **2.** a city in northern Kentucky. **3.** a town in western Virginia.

Lo ki (lō′ki), Norse god of destruction.

Ló pez (lō′pes).

Lou is ville (lü′i vil), city in northern Kentucky, on the Ohio River.

Lu i gi (lü ē′jē).

Ly ci a (lish′i ə), an ancient district in Asia Minor.

Ma ca ya (mä kä′yä).

Mag bo lo to (mäg′bō lō′tō).

---

hat, āge, cāre, fär; let, ēqual, tėrm; it, īce; hot, ōpen, ôrder; oil, out; cup, pùt, rüle, ūse; ch, child; ng, long; sh, she; th, thin; ŦH, then; zh, measure; ə represents *a* in about, *e* in taken, *i* in pencil, *o* in lemon, *u* in circus.

Mag nif i cat (mag nif′ə kät), Our Lady's song of praise to God at the time of her Visitation to her cousin Elizabeth before Jesus was born. **Magnificat** is the first word of the Latin form of the prayer, which begins, "My soul magnifies the Lord."

mag ni fy (mag′nə fī), **1.** cause to look larger than it really is: *A microscope is a magnifying glass.* **2.** praise highly; laud.

mag pie (mag′pī), a black-and-white bird that chatters a great deal. Magpies like to imitate the notes of other birds, and when tamed they can learn to speak simple words.

mail (māl), material of linked metal pieces used to make protective garments. **Chain mail** is made with interlinked loops of fine chain.

mailed (māld), covered with mail or other metal.

ma li cious (mə lish′əs), spiteful; showing ill will; wishing to hurt or make suffer: *a malicious telltale.*

ma neu ver (mə nü′vər), **1.** a planned movement of troops or warships. **2.** perform maneuvers; cause troops to perform maneuvers. **3.** a movement that is hard to follow, or deceives the eye or the mind. **4.** carry out such a movement or maneuver; manipulate skillfully.

Ma nil a (mə nil′ə), largest city of the Philippine Islands.

man or (man′ər), **1.** a large piece of land owned by a nobleman. In the Middle Ages the land was divided into several parts, a large one for the lord of the manor, and small plots for his peasants. (See **peasant.**) If the lord sold his manor, the peasants were sold with it. **2.** house or mansion of a landed estate; manor house.

Mar co ni (mär kō′ni), **Guglielmo** (gül yel′mō), 1874-1937, Italian inventor who perfected the wireless telegraph.

ma rine (mə rēn′), of the sea; found in the sea; produced by the sea.

me an der (mi an′dər), **1.** to wind about: *a river that meanders.* **2.** to wander aimlessly: *We were meandering through the park.*

me di e val (mē′di ē′vəl), having to do with the Middle Ages (the years from about 500 A.D. to about 1450 A.D.).

Med i ter ra ne an (med′ə tə rā′ni ən), the sea between Europe and Africa.

mel an chol y (mel′ən kol′i), **1.** sadness; low spirits; tendency to be sad. **2.** sad; gloomy: *A melancholy man is not good company.* **3.** causing sadness: *a melancholy scene.*

Mess ire (mes ēr′), a title of respect given to French noblemen and other persons of quality long ago.

Mi chael (mi′kəl).

mil let (mil′it), a grain used for food in Asia and in southern Europe. In the United States, millet is grown chiefly for hay.

min strel (min′strəl), **1.** a singer or musician in the household of a lord in the Middle Ages. **2.** a singer or musician who went about and sang or recited poems, often of his own making: *The wandering medieval minstrels helped to preserve for us the hero tales and folk legends of olden times.*

mod er ate (mod′ər it for 1 and 2, mod′ər āt for 3), **1.** kept or keeping within proper bounds; not extreme: *moderate expenses, moderate styles.* **2.** fair; medium; not very large or good: *to make a moderate profit.* **3.** make less violent; become less extreme: *The wind is moderating.*

mor al (môr′əl), **1.** the lesson, inner meaning, or teaching of a fable, a story, or an event. **2.** having to do with character, or with the difference between right and wrong.

mo sa ic (mō zā′ik), **1.** small pieces of stone, glass, wood, etc., of different colors inlaid to form a design. **2.** a picture or design formed by such work.

mu nic i pal i ty (mū nis′ə pal′ə ti), city, town, or other district having local self-government.

munt jac (munt′jak).

mus ter (mus′tər), **1.** assemble; gather together; collect. **2.** summon: *to muster up courage.*

Myn heer (mīn hār′), a Dutch word meaning sir or Mr.

myr tle (mėr′təl), **1.** evergreen shrub of S. Europe which has shiny leaves, fragrant white or rosy flowers, and black berries. **2.** in the U.S., a low, creeping evergreen plant with blue flowers.

nat u ral ist (nach′ə rəl ist), person who makes a study of animals and plants.

na wab (nə wôb′), **1.** a native ruler in India under the Mogul empire. **2.** a title given to important Mohammedans in India.

neg a tive (neg′ə tiv), **1.** saying no: *His answer was negative.* **2.** the side that says no or denies in an argument. **3.** minus; counting down from zero: *Three below zero is a negative quantity.* **4.** a photographic image in which the lights and shadows are reversed. Prints are made from it.

Ne ri (nā′ri), Philip, 16th century saint known for his cheerfulness. He is called the Apostle of Rome.

New found land (nü′fənd land′ or nü′fənd land′), a large island east of Canada.

no to ri ous (nō tô′ri əs), well-known or commonly known, especially because of something bad.

nov ice (nov′is), **1.** beginner; one who is new to what he is doing: *Novices are likely to make some mistakes.* **2.** person who is preparing for a life as a nun or monk by a period of trial and prayer before making solemn vows to God.

nymph (nimf), a lesser goddess of nature, who lived in seas, rivers, fountains, hills, woods, or trees.

ob sta cle (ob′stə kəl), something that stands in the way, or stops progress.

ob struct (əb strukt′), **1.** block up; make hard to pass through: *Fallen trees obstructed the road.* **2.** be in the way of; hinder: *Trees obstructed our view of the ocean.*

ob struc tion (əb struk′shən), **1.** thing that obstructs; something in the way. **2.** blocking; hindering.

ob vi ous (ob′vi əs), plain; easily seen or understood; clear to the eye or mind; not to be doubted.

O hal la (ō hal′ə).

o ka pi (ō kä′pi), an African animal like the giraffe, but smaller and with a much shorter neck.

Onst wed de (ônst′ved′ə).

op press (ə pres′), **1.** govern harshly; keep down unjustly or by cruelty. **2.** weigh down; lie heavily on.

op pres sion (ə presh′ən), **1.** oppressing; burdening: *The nobles' oppression of the people caused the war.* **2.** condition of being unjustly burdened: *They fought against oppression.* **3.** cruel treatment.

Pak i stan (pak′ə stan or pä′kə-stän), country in southern Asia, a republic since 1956, but once part of India and under British rule.

---

hat, āge, cãre, fär; let, ēqual, tėrm; it, īce; hot, ōpen, ôrder; oil, out; cup, pút, rüle, ūse; ch, child; ng, long; sh, she; th, thin; ₮H, then; zh, measure; ə represents *a* in about, *e* in taken, *i* in pencil, *o* in lemon, *u* in circus.

Panna Marya (pän′nä mer′yä), the church of Our Lady Mary in Krakow, Poland.

Paz (päs).

peas ant (pez′ənt), **1.** outside the U.S., one who lives and works on the land; farmer who works a small piece of land. **2.** in the Middle Ages, one of the class of people who were assigned to farm a small plot of land on the lord's estate, and had to pay him rent or tax out of the proceeds.

Pe dro (pā′drō).

Peg a sus (peg′ə səs), a horse with wings, the steed of the Muses.

Pe pe (pā′pā).

per chance (pər chans′), perhaps.

per pet u al (pər pech′ü al), **1.** eternal; lasting forever; lasting throughout life: *the perpetual hills.* **2.** continuous; never ceasing: *a disease that puts a person in perpetual pain.*

Pe ru gia (pə rü′jə), city in central Italy.

pe ti tion (pə tish′ən), **1.** formal request. **2.** ask earnestly; make a petition to: *They petitioned the mayor to use his influence with the city council.*

Phil ip pine (fil′ə pēn), of or having to do with the Philippines or their inhabitants.

Philippine Islands, Philippines.

Phil ip pines (fil′ə pēnz), group of 7083 islands in the West Pacific Ocean, southeast of Asia and north of Australia. The Philippines were under the guardianship of the United States until 1946, when they received their independence.

Pi e tro (pi ā′trō).

pil grim (pil′grəm), **1.** person who goes on a journey to a sacred or holy place as an act of religious devotion. **2.** traveler. **3.** one of the English settlers who founded Plymouth, Massachusetts, in 1620.

pin a fore (pin′ə fôr′), a child's apron that covers most of the dress.

plaid (plad), **1.** a long piece of woolen cloth, usually having a pattern of checks or stripes in many colors, worn about the shoulders by the Scottish Highlanders. **2.** having a pattern of checks or stripes: *a plaid dress.*

pla toon (plə tün′), **1.** a group of soldiers acting as a unit. A platoon is smaller than a company and larger than a squad. **2.** small group.

plum met (plum′it), **1.** a weight fastened to a line; plumb. **2.** plunge; drop.

poach[1] (pōch), **1.** trespass on another's land, especially to hunt or fish. **2.** take (game or fish) without any right.

POMMEL

poach[2] (pōch), cook (an egg) by breaking it into boiling water.

pom mel (pum′əl), **1.** the part of a saddle that sticks up at the front. **2.** strike or beat; beat with the fists.

pre lim i nar y (pri lim′ə ner′i), coming before the main business; leading to something more important.

pre side (pri zīd′), **1.** hold the place of authority; have charge of a meeting: *Our principal will preside at our election of school officers.* **2.** have authority; have control: *The manager presides over the business of the store.*

prod (prod), **1.** poke with something pointed. **2.** stir up; urge on; goad. **3.** a poke; a thrust: *That prod in the ribs hurt.* **4.** a sharp-pointed stick; a goad.

Proe tus (prē′təs).

pro fu sion (prə fü′zhən), great abundance.

pro pos al (prə pōz′əl), **1.** plan; scheme; suggestion. **2.** act of proposing.

pro pose (prə pōz′),　put forward; suggest.

pros trate (pros′trāt), **1.** lay down flat; cast down: *The captives prostrated themselves before the conqueror.* **2.** lying flat or face downward.

pro trude (prō trüd′),　**1.** thrust forth; stick out: *The saucy child protruded her tongue.* **2.** be thrust forth; project: *Her teeth protruded too far.*

prov ince (prov′əns), **1.** a part of a country at a distance from the capital. **2.** a big division of a country. Canada is divided into provinces instead of into States. **3.** a division; a department: *the province of science.* **4.** proper work or activity: *Teaching spelling is not within the province of a college.*

Puer to Ri co (pwer′- tō rē′kō),　island in the eastern part of the West Indies. Puerto Rico became a commonwealth in 1952, and is under the protection of the United States.

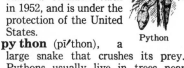

Python

py thon (pī′thon),　a large snake that crushes its prey. Pythons usually live in trees near water.

qual i ty (kwol′ə ti), **1.** something special about an object that makes it what it is: *One quality of iron is hardness; one quality of sugar is sweetness.* **2.** the kind that anything is: *That is a poor quality of cloth.* **3.** fineness; merit; excellence: *Look for quality rather than quantity.*

quar an tine (kwôr′ən tēn), **1.** keep (a person, etc., having an infectious disease) away from others: *James was quarantined for three weeks when he*

had scarlet fever. **2.** state of being quarantined: *Our house was in quarantine for three weeks when we had scarlet fever.* **3.** time during which ships coming into large ports are held until doctors have made sure that there is no infectious disease on board.

quest (kwest), **1.** a search; a hunt. **2.** to search; to seek. **3.** expedition made by knights: *There are many stories about the quest of the Holy Grail.*

Ram pur (räm′pur).

reach (rēch), **1.** get to; arrive at; come to: *Your letter reached me yesterday.* **2.** stretch out; hold out: *A hand reached from the dark and seized Jack.* **3.** a long stretch or extent: *a reach of woodland, a reach of water.* **4.** a portion of a river between bends.

re buke (ri būk′), **1.** express strong disapproval of; reprove sharply or sternly: *Jesus rebuked the dishonest moneychangers in the Temple.* **2.** a stern correction; a scolding.

re gal (rē′gəl), **1.** belonging to a king; royal: *The regal power descends from father to son.* **2.** kinglike; fit for a king: *It was a regal banquet.*

re prieve (ri prēv′), **1.** delay the execution of (a person condemned to death): *At the last moment the prisoner was reprieved for three weeks.* **2.** a delay in carrying out a punishment, especially of the death penalty.

re prove (ri prüv′),　find fault with; disapprove; blame for wrong-doing: *His father reproved Tom for lying.*

re tain er (ri tān′ər), an attendant; a servant, especially to a person of high position or rank.

Ro sar io (rō sär′yō).

Ros kva (rôs′kvä).

Ru iz (rü ēs′).

---

hat, āge, cãre, fär; let, ēqual, tėrm; it, īce; hot, ōpen, ôrder; oil, out; cup, put, rüle, ūse; ch, child; ng, long; sh, she; th, thin; ᴛʜ, then; zh, measure; ə represents *a* in about, *e* in taken, *i* in pencil, *o* in lemon, *u* in circus.

Sa co (sä′kō).

saf fron (saf′rən), **1.** an orange-yellow coloring and flavoring matter obtained from a kind of crocus. **2.** bright orange-yellow in color.

Sar a cen (sar′ə sən), **1.** an Arab; one of the Arabs who settled around the Holy Land and formed the Moslem Empire. **2.** a Mohammedan at the time of the Crusades. The Crusaders called their enemies **Saracens** even though the cruelest of them were not Arabs but barbarians who had conquered the Arabs.

sa ri (sä′ri), a long piece of cotton or silk, the outer garment of Hindu women, worn wound around the body with one end thrown over the head.

scor pi on (skôr′pi ən), a small animal belonging to the same group as the spider and having a poisonous sting in its tail.

Scorpion (1 to 8 in. long)

Scot land (skot′lənd), the division of Great Britain north of England; the land of the Scotch.

Scot tish (skot′ish), of or having to do with Scotland, its people, or their language.

scrub (skrub), low, stunted trees or shrubs: *Scrub pine was coming up in the pasture.*

se clud ed (si klüd′id), shut off from others; undisturbed.

sec re tar y (sek′rə ter′i), **1.** person who writes letters, keeps records, etc., for a person, company, club, etc.: *Our club has a secretary who keeps the minutes of the meetings. Mr. Jones keeps three secretaries busy.* **2.** person who has charge of a department of a government. The Secretary of the Treasury is the head of the Treasury Department.

sep ul cher (sep′əl kər), place of burial; tomb; grave.

se rene (sə rēn′), **1.** peaceful; calm: *serene happiness, a serene smile.* **2.** clear; bright; not cloudy.

Ser va re Fi dem (ser vä′rā fē′-dem).

ser vi tor (sèr′və tər), servant; attendant.

sheaf (shēf), bundle of things of the same sort: *a sheaf of wheat, a sheaf of arrows.*

sheaves (shēvz), more than one sheaf.

Shreve port (shrēv′pôrt), a city in northwestern Louisiana.

shun (shun), keep away from; avoid: *She was lazy and shunned work.*

si gnor (sē′nyōr), an Italian word meaning sir or Mr.

si gno ra (sē nyō′rä), an Italian word meaning Mrs.

si mul ta ne ous ly (sī′məl tā′ni-əs li), at once; at the same time.

smite (smīt), strike; strike hard; hit hard: *The hero smote the giant with his sword. His conscience smote him. She was smitten with curiosity about the forbidden room.*

Smith so ni an Institution (smith sō′ni ən), institution in Washington, D.C., founded to increase and spread knowledge by providing money for scientific research and for exhibits of discoveries and inventions.

smote (smōt). See **smite.**

som ber or **som bre** (som′bər), **1.** dark; gloomy: *It was a somber room with dark furniture and black hangings.* **2.** melancholy; dismal: *His losses made him very somber.*

spurn (spèrn), **1.** scorn; refuse with scorn: *The judge spurned the bribe.* **2.** strike with the foot; kick away.

squire (skwīr), in the Middle Ages, a young man of noble family who attended a knight until he himself was made a knight.

sta lac tite (stə lak′tīt), a formation of lime, shaped like an icicle, hanging from the roof of a cave. Stalactites and stalagmites are formed by dripping water that contains lime.

sta lag mite (stə lag′mīt), a formation of lime, shaped like a cone, built up on the floor of a cave.

stal wart (stôl′wərt), **1.** strongly built. **2.** strong and brave. **3.** firm.

sta tion (stā′shən), **1.** place to stand in. **2.** a building or place used for a definite purpose. A place where soldiers live, a harbor for ships, and the police headquarters of a district are all called stations. **3.** place or equipment for sending out or receiving programs, messages, etc., by radio. **4.** regular stopping place: *Father met Kate at the railroad station.*

step broth er (step′bruᴛʜ′ər), a stepfather's or stepmother's son by a former marriage: *If John's father marries a widow with a little boy, this boy will be John's stepbrother.*

step moth er (step′muᴛʜ′ər), woman who has married one's father after the death or divorce of one's real mother.

sti let to (stə let′ō),

Stiletto

a dagger with a narrow blade.

St. Mar tins-de-Bou chage (san mär tan′də bü shäzh′).

stock y (stok′i), having a solid form or build, thick for its height.

stoke (stōk), poke, stir up, and feed (a fire); tend the fire of (a furnace).

sub-, a prefix that means:
1. under; below; as in *subway, submarine.*
2. near; as in *subconscious.*

3. slightly; somewhat; as in *subacid.*
4. of less importance; as in *subhead.*

sub merge (səb mėrj′), **1.** put under water: *A big wave submerged us.* **2.** cover with water: *At high tide this path is submerged.* **3.** sink under water: *The submarine submerged to escape being destroyed.*

sub sta tion (sub′stā′shən), a branch station: *Besides the main post office in our city, there are six substations.*

sub ter ra ne an (sub′tə rā′ni ən), **1.** underground: *A subterranean passage led from the castle to a cave.* **2.** carried on secretly: *a subterranean plotting.*

su perb (sù pėrb′), **1.** grand; stately; majestic: *Mountain scenery is superb. The queen's jewels are superb.* **2.** very fine; excellent: *The actor gave a superb performance.*

su per vise (sü′pər vīz), look after and direct (work or workers, a process, etc.); oversee; superintend; manage: *Study halls are supervised by teachers.*

swart (swôrt), having a dark skin.

swath (swôth), **1.** the space covered by a single cut of a scythe; one cut of a mowing machine. **2.** row of grass, grain, etc., cut by a scythe or mowing machine.

tack le (tak′əl), equipment; apparatus; gear. Ropes and pulleys for lifting furniture through windows are called tackle; so are the ropes that work the sails of a ship. **Fishing tackle** means the rod, line, hooks, etc.

Tackles for lifting

---

hat, āge, cãre, fär; let, ēqual, tėrm; it, īce; hot, ōpen, ôrder; oil, out; cup, pùt, rüle, ūse; ch, child; ng, long; sh, she; th, thin; ᴛʜ, then; zh, measure; ə represents *a* in about, *e* in taken, *i* in pencil, *o* in lemon, *u* in circus.

Tagh Mor (ŦHĭg′ mōr′).

tal is man (tal′is mən), **1.** an object engraved with markings supposed to have magic power; a charm. **2.** anything given as a token of fond regard and worn or carried as a reminder of the giver. *Used in poetry.*

teal (tēl), small fresh-water duck.

tem per ate (tem′pər it), not very hot, and not very cold: *The United States is mostly in the north temperate zone.*

thatch (thach), **1.** straw, rushes, or the like, used to cover roofs or stacks. **2.** cover with thatch.

thence (ŦHens), **1.** from that place. **2.** for that reason. **3.** from that time.

Thi al fi (thi äl′vi).

thor ough fare (thèr′ō fãr′), **1.** a passage, road, or street open at both ends. **2.** main road; highway.

ti dings (tī′dingz), news; information.

tilt yard (tilt′yärd′), a yard or enclosed space for tilts and tournaments; a tilting-ground.

Ti tan (tī′tən), **1.** in Greek mythology, one of a family of giants who ruled the world. Prometheus and Atlas were Titans. **2.** A **titan** is a person or thing having enormous size, strength, power, etc.; a giant.

Ton to (tŏn′tō).

tor rid (tôr′id), very hot: *Brazil is in the torrid zone. July is a torrid month.*

tour na ment (tèr′nə mənt), **1.** contest between two groups of knights on horseback who fought for a prize; jousts. **2.** a group sports contest.

trag e dy (traj′ə di), **1.** serious play having an unhappy ending. Shakespeare's play *Hamlet* is a tragedy. **2.** very sad or terrible happening: *The father's sudden death was a tragedy to his family.*

trag ic (traj′ik), **1.** of tragedy; having to do with tragedy: *a tragic actor.*

2. very sad; dreadful: *a tragic death, a tragic event.*

tran quil (trang′kwəl), calm; peaceful; quiet.

trans-, a prefix meaning across, over, through, beyond, or on the other side of, as in *transcontinental* or *transmarine.*

trans at lan tic (trans′ət lan′tik), crossing the Atlantic: *a transatlantic liner, a transatlantic cable.*

trans mit (trans mit′), **1.** send over; pass on; pass along; let through: *I will transmit the money by special messenger. Rats transmit disease.* **2.** send out (signals, voice, music, etc.) by radio.

trans mit ter (trans mit′ər), **1.** person or thing that transmits something. **2.** that part of a telegraph or telephone by which messages are sent. **3.** apparatus for sending out signals, music, etc., by radio.

trans par ent (trans pãr′ənt), **1.** easily seen through: *Window glass is transparent.* **2.** clear: *a boy of transparent honesty.*

trans port (trans pôrt′ for 1, trans′pôrt for 2), **1.** carry from one place to another: *Wheat is transported from the farms to the mills.* **2.** carrying from one place to another: *Trucks are much used for transport.*

trans por ta tion (trans′pôr tā′shən), **1.** transporting; being transported: *The railroad gives free transportation for a certain amount of baggage.* **2.** means of transport.

treach er ous (trech′ər əs), **1.** not to be trusted; not faithful: *The treacherous soldier carried reports to the enemy.* **2.** deceiving; not reliable; having a false appearance of strength, security, etc.: *The thin ice is treacherous.*

treach er y (trech′ər i), **1.** deceit; breaking faith; treacherous behavior. **2.** treason.

trop ic (trop′ik), **1.** either of the two circles around the earth, one 23.45 degrees north and one 23.45 degrees south of the equator. **2. The tropics** often means the regions between these circles: *It is hot in the tropics.* **3.** of the tropics.

tu mult (tü′mult), **1.** noise; uproar. **2.** violent disturbance or disorder.

tur ban (tèr′bən), a scarf wound around the head or around a cap, worn by men in Oriental countries.

tur ret (tèr′it), **1.** small tower, often on a corner of a building. **2.** revolving armored structure for mounting guns.

twine (twīn), **1.** a strong thread or string made of two or more strands twisted together. **2.** twist together: *She twined holly into wreaths.* **3.** wind: *The vine twines around the tree.*

un du la tion (un′jú lā′shən), **1.** waving motion. **2.** wavy form. **3.** one of a series of wavelike bends, curves, swellings, etc.

un wield y (un wēl′di), hard to handle or manage; not easy to use or control because of size, shape, or weight; clumsy: *The armor worn by knights seems unwieldy to us today.*

Van Hoorn (vän′ hōrn′).

veg e tar i an (vej′ə tär′i ən), **1.** person who eats vegetables but no meat. **2.** eating vegetables but no meat.

veg e ta tion (vej′ə tā′shən), plant life; growing plants; growth of plants: *There is not much vegetation in deserts.*

ve loc i ty (və los′ə ti), **1.** speed; swiftness; quickness. **2.** rate of motion: *A bullet goes from this gun with a velocity of 3000 feet a second.*

ven i son (ven′ə zən), deer meat; the flesh of a deer, used for food.

ve ran da or **ve ran dah** (və ran′-də), large porch along one or more sides of a house.

ves pers (ves′pərz), **1.** church service held in the late afternoon or evening. **2.** a part of the Divine Office said or sung by priests and nuns in the late afternoon.

Vi a na (vi ä′nə).

Vi aud (vi ō′).

vi zier or **vi zir** (vi zēr′), high official in Mohammedan countries; minister of state.

watt (wot), a unit of electric power: *My lamp uses 60 watts; my toaster uses 660 watts.*

wince (wins), draw back suddenly; shrink.

wit (wit), **1.** the power to perceive quickly and express cleverly ideas that are unusual, striking, and amusing. **2.** a person with such power. **3.** understanding; mind; sense: *People with quick wits learn easily.*

woe be gone or **wo be gone** (wō′bi gôn′), woeful; looking sad; sorrowful; wretched.

yeo man (yō′mən), **1.** in the United States Navy, a petty officer who performs clerical duties. **2.** in England, a person who owns land, but not a large amount. **3.** a servant or attendant of a lord or king.

yew (ū), **1.** an evergreen tree of Europe and Asia. **2.** the wood of this tree.

zeal (zēl), earnest enthusiasm; eager desire: *The boys worked with zeal at learning to drive the car.*

---

hat, āge, cãre, fär; let, ēqual, tèrm; it, īce; hot, ōpen, ôrder; oil, out; cup, pùt, rüle, ūse; ch, child; ng, long; sh, she; th, thin; ᴛʜ, then; zh, measure; ə represents *a* in about, *e* in taken, *i* in pencil, *o* in lemon, *u* in circus.

TO THE TEACHER

More People and Progress, Book 6², with its accompanying *Guidebook* and *Think-and-Do Book,* continues The New Cathedral Basic Reading Program for the middle grades. It is designed for approximately one semester's use whenever the child has successfully completed the new *People and Progress.*

More People and Progress contains 822 words not introduced by the end of Book 6¹ of The New Cathedral Basic Reading Program. In the first unit of *More People and Progress,* no page has more than seven new words, and no page in the entire book introduces more than eight new words.

The 822 new words in this book are shown in the vocabulary list below. The following forms of known words are not counted as new (including those forms made by changing *y* to *i* or *f* to *v,* by dropping the final *e,* or by doubling the final consonant in the root word): forms made by adding or dropping the inflectional ending *s, es, ed, ing, n, en,* and *er, est* of comparison; possessives; forms made by adding or dropping the prefixes *a-, be-, dis-, fore-, il-, im-, in-, ir-, out-, over-, re-, un-,* or *under-,* and the suffixes *-able, -al, -ally, -ation, -en, -er, -ful, -ion, -ish, -less, -ly, -ment, -ness, -or, -ous, -ship, -ward,* or *-y,* and *-teen, -th,* or *-ty* of numerals; compounds made up of known words; common contractions. Homographs are not counted as separate words; for example, if *forge* meaning "place with fire where metal is heated very hot and then hammered into shape" has been introduced, *forge* meaning "move forward slowly but steadily" is not counted as a separate word. Nonsense words, syllables that represent sounds, and the following foreign words are not counted: *Juffrouw, Mynheer, servare, fidem, adiós, señor, muchas, gracias, barrio, nawab, tongas, rickshas, saris, curry, chappatti, poppars, chital, muntjacs, bongo, okapi, dom, signora, signor, Messire, Bejaunus, ave, atque, vale.*

Boys and girls can attack independently all of the 822 new words by applying the word-analysis and dictionary skills developed in The New Cathedral Basic Reading Program. The words printed in italics in the vocabulary list are included in the glossary of *More People and Progress.*

VOCABULARY LIST

UNIT I

6 *Kaatje*
Karel
petticoats
Koopdam
Bloemen
bodice ,

7 blond
braids
trousers
Van Hoorn
council
guilders
8 .....

9 tulips
bedecked
garlands
10 *Frans*
Annetje
11 Ferris
12 nevertheless
beforehand

13 rung
14 soggy
15 stranded
Kees
16 *stocky*
17 blurted
18 apologetically

314

316

317

318

ILLUSTRATIONS

The pictures in this book were made by: Joe Pearson (cover, 5, 61, 121, 177, 239); Seymour Fleishman (1, 3, 282–289); Henry M. Picken (2, 19–25, 101, 178–185, 212–238); Eleanor Dart (6-16, 41–48); John Merryweather (26–33, 49, 71–75, 91, 131–140, 257, 280–281); Robert Doremus (35–40); A. K. Builder (50–60, 258–263, 273–278); James Teason (62–69); I. Heilbron (76, 119); Else Bostleman (78–87); Robert Kuhn (92–100, 107–117); Willard Arnold (102–106); Chauncey Maltman (122–129, 160–169); Raymon Naylor (143–159, 170–176); Robert S. Robison (187–211); Jack White (240–254); Nathan Goldstein (264–271); M. S. Hurford (291, 292).

ACKNOWLEDGMENTS

For permission to adapt and use copyrighted material, grateful acknowledgment is made to the following:

To the author and the publishers for "Kaatje's Adventure" from *Kaatje and the Christmas Compass* by Alta Halverson Seymour, copyright 1954 by Alta Halverson Seymour, published by Wilcox & Follett Company, Chicago, Illinois; to the author and to St. Martin's Press, Inc., and Macmillan & Company, Ltd. for "A Heritage to Treasure" from *Heritage* by Hilda K. F. Gull; to the author for "Two Days to Remember" by Kathryn Bilterman; to the publishers for "A Good Bargain" from "Kimba and the Crows' Eggs" by Murray T. Pringle, copyright, 1952, by Story Parade, Inc., reprinted by permission; to the author for "Surprise in Manila" by Carmen Adriano; to the publishers, the author, and Lyle H. Bean for "I Take a Look at the World" from "Beanie Takes a Look at the World" by Elizabeth Bean in *Collier's.*

To the author and publishers for "Penguin Parade" by Murray T. Pringle in *Venture;* to the author and publishers for "Biggest Wild Animal Business" by David A. Shulman in *American Boy;* to the author and publishers for "The Shining Gateway" by Hubert Evans in *Boy's Life.*

To Batten, Barton, Durstine, and Osborn, Inc., and the author for "The River Finds a Master" from a *Cavalcade of America* script based on material from *Lost Men of American History* by Stewart Holbrook; to the publishers for "Machine Crazy," a selection from *Henry Ford, Engineer* by Louise A. Neyhart, reprinted by permission of and arrangement with Houghton Mifflin Company, the authorized publisher.

To the author and publishers for "Little Dusty Foot" from *Little Dusty Foot* by Marian W. Magoon, published by Longmans, Green and Co., Inc., copyright 1948; to the author and publisher for "Sunday in Assisi" by Ivy Bolton in *The Ave Maria;* to the publisher for "Gabriel and the Hour Book" from *Gabriel and the Hour Book* by Evaleen Stein, published by L. C. Page & Company, Inc., a subsidiary of Farrar, Straus and Cudahy, Inc., 101 Fifth Avenue, New York 3, N.Y.; to the author and publisher for "The Maker of Maps" adapted from "The Maker of Maps" from *Strange Sea Stories* by Marie A. Lawson, copyright 1955 by Marie A. Lawson, reprinted by permission of The Viking Press, Inc.

To the publishers for "Ali Cogia and the Olives" from "Ali Cogia, Merchant of Bagdad" from *Arabian Nights,* edited by Andrew Lang, copyright 1946, Longmans, Green and Company, Inc.; to the author for "The Adventures of Magboloto" from *Once in the First Times* by Elizabeth Hough Sechrist, published by Macrae Smith Company, copyright 1949; to the publisher for "Magnificat of the Heart" from "Magnificat of the Dumb" in *The Silver Legend* by I. A. Taylor, published by Sands and Company, Ltd.

4 5 6 7 8 9 10 11 12 13 14 15 16 17 18 19 20 21 22 23 24 25   F   66 65